TUTOR ASSESSMENT PACK

MATHEMATICS

— GCSE —

HIGHER

Author: Sharon Bolger

Edexcel

Contents

Edexcel

Contents

MATHS HIGHER

How to use this pack

This *Tutors' Guild* Maths Higher Tutor Assessment Pack is full of assessment opportunities to help you prepare your student for the Edexcel GCSE (9–1) Mathematics Higher exam. You can keep a record of your student's achievements using the progress tracker on the contents pages.

Types of test

The pack comprises three types of test, detailed below.

Topic tests

For every lesson in the Tutor Delivery Pack, there is a topic test. These short tests each have 10 marks and should take around 20 minutes to complete. They have the same friendly, accessible look as the Tutor Delivery Pack activity sheets, to make assessment much less stressful for your student while allowing you to regularly and effectively track progress.

As with every aspect of the *Tutors' Guild* series, topic tests are designed to be completely flexible. Tutors with more than an hour per lesson may choose to complete the test at the end of the lesson or at the beginning of the next, to test knowledge retention. Equally, the tests are short enough that they can be given to students to complete during the week, instead of or alongside the suggested homework activity for the lesson. You may also wish to use the topic tests to revisit topics with which your student struggled when completing the checkpoint challenges or practice papers.

Checkpoint challenges

These tests are designed to each assess one subject area from the Mathematics curriculum: number; algebra; ratio, proportion and rates of change; geometry and measures; probability; and statistics. Each challenge should take around 30 minutes to complete, but they don't need to be strictly timed.

Each challenge will cover content taught during the corresponding lessons in the *Tutors' Guild* Edexcel GCSE Maths Higher Tutor Delivery Pack (ISBN: 9781292195797). Checkpoint challenges are not designed to be exam-style but the content they cover is taken from the Edexcel GCSE (9–1) Mathematics specification (see pages 7–10 of the Tutor Delivery Pack for more on the specification). They replicate the style of the Tutor Delivery Pack activity sheets: familiar, unintimidating and engaging.

Checkpoint challenges can be used at any time during the course of tutoring – as a diagnostic at the beginning of the year or as revision before the tests, for example – but the most useful time to use them is at the end of each subject area as a summative test of your student's knowledge. The challenge may reveal an area in which your student lacks confidence, and assessment throughout the year gives you plenty of time to address those areas.

Practice papers

In order to successfully prepare your student for exam, you should ensure they have the chance to experience 'exam-style' assessment. The practice papers in this pack give your student the perfect opportunity to become accustomed to the layout and demands of the national curriculum tests. For more on the content and style of the tests, see pages 7–8.

To get the most out of the practice papers, you may wish to have your student complete them well in advance of the test. This will ensure you have time to address any difficulties that become apparent. As there are three papers, it is advisable to complete them over a period of several weeks, so as not to put your student under too much pressure.

Answers and mark schemes

Answers and mark schemes for all the tests are provided at the back of this pack. In the checkpoint challenge and practice paper mark schemes the following mark allocation abbreviations are used:

- M: method mark awarded for correct or partially correct method
- A: accuracy mark awarded only if a corresponding M mark has been achieved
- B: accuracy mark awarded independently of method

Pearson progression scale

Each question in this pack features a Step icon that indicates the level of challenge aligned to the Pearson Progression Map and Scale. To find out more about the Progression Scale for Maths and to see how it relates to indicative GCSE 9–1 grades go to www.pearsonschools.co.uk/ProgressionServices

How to use this pack

Progress tracking

On the contents page of this pack, you will find progress tracker columns to fill in every time your student completes an assessment. There is space on the tracker for you to record a first and second attempt at each test, if you wish to do so. When your student completes a test, look closely at the results and try to pick out patterns in their mistakes. Make a note of these patterns in the 'progress and observations' pages at the back of this book, so that you can use your future contact time together most effectively. You may wish to fill in the *Talk about the test* sheet (page 9) with your student to find out which questions they found the hardest to answer, particularly if the test doesn't reveal much because they didn't get many questions wrong.

Information for parents

The information for parents provided on pages 5–6 of this pack is very similar to that in the Tutor Delivery Pack. This has been repeated for tutors who have decided to purchase one of the packs but not the other. If the parents of your student have seen the information in the Tutor Delivery Pack, you may just wish to explain the different types of test to them.

Certificates

In the digital version of this pack, you will find two customisable certificates. These can be edited to celebrate achievements throughout the year.

Information for parents and guardians

Introduction

Your child's tutor will often make use of resources from the *Tutors' Guild* series. These resources have been produced especially for the new GCSE (9–1) assessments and are tailored for the Edexcel Mathematics specification. The tutor will use their expert knowledge and judgement to assess your child's current needs. This will allow them to target areas for improvement, build confidence levels and develop skills as quickly as possible, giving your child the best chance to succeed in their exam.

Just as a classroom teacher might do, the tutor will use practice papers and tests to prepare your child for their exam. Each set of resources has been designed by experts in GCSE (9–1) maths and reviewed by experienced classroom teachers and tutors to ensure it offers great quality, effective and enjoyable assessment.

Getting started

Before tuition can begin, the tutor will need to know more about your motives for employing them in order to set clear, achievable goals. They will also try to learn more about the student to ensure lessons are as useful and as engaging as possible. It shouldn't take too long to have this discussion with your tutor, but it will really maximise the value of the tuition time you pay for. You could also take the opportunity to address any questions or concerns you may have.

Types of test

Topic tests

Topic tests are short, 20-minute tests that are worth 10 marks each. They are designed to be fun and unintimidating for your child. They test much smaller areas (topics) of maths. Whereas there is a checkpoint challenge testing all number skills, there are individual topic tests for each of calculations, standard form, estimating and sequences, amongst others. There are 38 topic tests in total, which is enough for one per school week. Again, if your child completes a test for homework, you do not need to time their completion.

Checkpoint challenges

Checkpoint challenges are designed to test your child's knowledge of a whole area of maths. There are six challenges: number; algebra; ratio, proportion and rates of change; geometry and measures; probability; and statistics. The challenges are student-friendly in design, while still testing the topics your child will come across in the GCSE (9–1) exam.

Your tutor may decide to complete the challenges during teaching time. This may depend on your child's confidence levels or reading ability, or it may be that they want to assess your child more informally and to discuss the challenge while completing it. Otherwise, your tutor will give your child the challenge to complete for homework. Each test will take around thirty minutes to complete. If your child is completing the challenge for homework, you don't need to time them strictly.

Practice papers

The *practice papers* replicate the GCSE (9–1) exam. If your child is given a practice paper, you may want to provide a quiet environment and time it more strictly so their experience of the paper is closer to 'the real thing'.

Pearson progression scale

 Each question in this pack features a Step icon that indicates the level of challenge aligned to the Pearson Progression Map and Scale. To find out more about the Progression Scale for Maths and to see how it relates to indicative GCSE 9–1 grades go to www.pearsonschools.co.uk/ProgressionServices

Further support

Parents often ask a tutor what else they can do to support their child's learning or what resources they can buy to provide extra revision and practice. As a Pearson resource, *Tutors' Guild* has been designed to complement the popular *Revise* series. Useful titles you may wish to purchase include:

- *Revise* Edexcel GCSE (9–1) Mathematics Higher Revision Guide (ISBN: 9781447988090)
- *Revise* Edexcel GCSE (9–1) Mathematics Higher Revision Workbook (ISBN: 9781292210889)
- *Revise* Edexcel GCSE (9–1) Mathematics Higher Guided Revision Workbook (ISBN: 9781292213705)
- *Revise* Edexcel GCSE (9–1) Mathematics Higher Revision Cards (ISBN: 9781292173221)
- *Revise* Edexcel GCSE (9–1) Mathematics Higher Practice Papers Plus (ISBN: 9781292096315)

Edexcel

Information for parents and guardians

What's in the test?

You may have heard a lot about the new GCSE (9–1) qualifications from your child's school, from other parents or in the media. Here is a breakdown of the Edexcel GCSE (9–1) Mathematics exams.

The papers

Your child will sit three GCSE (9–1) Mathematics papers. The exam is tiered, which means all candidates sit either Foundation or Higher papers. Each paper is worth 80 marks – one third of the total marks available. Candidates are given 1 hour and 30 minutes to complete each paper.

Paper 1 is non-calculator, while calculators are allowed in Papers 2 and 3. The GCSE (9–1) qualifications see an increase in the amount of calculator-allowed assessment, from 50% to 66.6%.

Results and grades

GCSE results day is typically the third or fourth Thursday in August. It is the same day across the country, so you can find out the exact date online. On results day, the student will be given a slip of paper (or one per exam board, if the school hasn't collated them) with an overall grade for each GCSE. Grades for the GCSE qualifications are no longer given as letters (A*–U) but as numbers (9–1) instead. The diagram below shows roughly how the old-style grades translate to the new ones.

Previous grade	A*	A		B	C		D	E	F	G	U
New grade	9	8	7	6	5	4		3	2	1	U

As you can see, the new grade 9 is pitched higher than an A*. There is a wider spread of grades available for students whose target would previously have been a B/C. Because Mathematics is tiered, Foundation students will be able to access grades 1–5, whereas Higher students should be aiming to achieve grades 4–9.

6

Edexcel

MATHS HIGHER

Assessment guidance

The new Edexcel GCSE (9–1) Maths qualification was introduced for first teaching in 2015 and first assessment in 2017. These pages will provide an overview of the assessments. It is recommended that you also familiarise yourself with the full specification on the Edexcel website.

The content domains

The new GCSE (9–1) content is more challenging than previous qualifications. New topics have been introduced, and the Foundation papers will now feature topics that were previously Higher only. These include standard form, index laws and vectors – a complete list is available on the Edexcel website. In terms of content domains, Ratio, proportion and rates of change is now a standalone area, and the Statistics and probability domain has been reduced in weighting. The table below shows how the content domains are weighted for the Higher papers.

Content domain	Weighting
Number	15%
Algebra	30%
Ratio, proportion and rates of change	20%
Geometry and measures	20%
Statistics and probability	15%

Assessment objectives

The GCSE (9–1) specification places an increased emphasis on problem solving and mathematical reasoning, both of which are skills that students often find challenging. AO2 now also assess quality of written communication. The table below shows the assessment objectives and their weighting in Higher tier.

Objective	Descriptor	Weighting
AO1	Use and apply standard techniques	40%
AO2	Reason, interpret and communicate mathematically	30%
AO3	Solve problems within mathematics and in other contexts	30%

Exam papers

Both Foundation and Higher students will sit three equally-weighted exam papers:

- Paper 1; non-calculator; 80 marks; 1.5 hours
- Paper 2; calculator; 80 marks; 1.5 hours
- Paper 3; calculator; 80 marks; 1.5 hours

Each paper will cover all five content domains, and will feature a range of structured, unstructured and contextual questions.

Grades

Edexcel GCSE (9–1) Maths is graded using the new 9–1 system. This means that on results day students will receive a number from 1 to 9 instead of a letter from A* to U. The diagram below shows roughly how the old-style grades equate to the new ones.

Previous grade		A*	A	B	C		D	E	F	G	U
New grade	9	8	7	6	5	4	3	2	1		U

The change is intended to better differentiate students of different abilities. A grade 9 is higher than an A*, and will be awarded to fewer students. There is also a wider spread of grades available to students who would previously been working towards a B or C.

A grade 4 is considered the closest equivalent to a C. Because Mathematics is tiered, Foundation students will be able to access grades 1–5, whereas Higher students should be aiming to achieve grades 4–9.

MATHS HIGHER

Assessment guidance

Required formulae

Fewer formulae will be provided in the exam than previously. The table below shows those formulae that students will need to know.

A poster highlighting them can be found on the Edexcel website.

Foundation students need to know the following:

Area	
rectangle = $l \times w$	parallelogram = $b \times h$
triangle = $\frac{1}{2}b \times h$	trapezium = $\frac{1}{2}(a + b)h$

Volume	
cuboid = $l \times w \times h$	cylinder = $\pi r^2 h$
prism = area of cross section × length	

Circles	
circumference = π × diameter	$C = \pi d$
circumference = 2 × π × radius	$C = 2\pi r$
area of circle = π × radius squared	$A = \pi r^2$

Compound measures	
speed = $\dfrac{\text{distance}}{\text{time}}$	density = $\dfrac{\text{mass}}{\text{volume}}$
The formula for pressure will be provided if relevant.	

Pythagoras
Pythagoras' Theorem: for a right-angled triangle, $a^2 + b^2 = c^2$
trigonometric ratios:
$\sin x = \dfrac{\text{opp}}{\text{hyp}}$ $\cos x = \dfrac{\text{adj}}{\text{hyp}}$ $\tan x = \dfrac{\text{opp}}{\text{adj}}$

Higher students need to know the following:

Area	
rectangle = $l \times w$	parallelogram = $b \times h$
triangle = $\frac{1}{2}b \times h$	trapezium = $\frac{1}{2}(a + b)h$

Volume	
cuboid = $l \times w \times h$	cylinder = $\pi r^2 h$
prism = area of cross section × length	
pyramid = $\frac{1}{3}$ × area of base × h	

Circles	
circumference = π × diameter	$C = \pi d$
circumference = 2 × π × radius	$C = 2\pi r$
area of circle = π × radius squared	$A = \pi r^2$

Compound measures	
speed = $\dfrac{\text{distance}}{\text{time}}$	density = $\dfrac{\text{mass}}{\text{volume}}$
The formula for pressure will be provided if relevant.	

Pythagoras
Pythagoras' Theorem: for a right-angled triangle, $a^2 + b^2 = c^2$
trigonometric ratios:
$\sin x = \dfrac{\text{opp}}{\text{hyp}}$ $\cos x = \dfrac{\text{adj}}{\text{hyp}}$ $\tan x = \dfrac{\text{opp}}{\text{adj}}$

Trigonometric formulae
sine rule $\dfrac{a}{\sin A} = \dfrac{b}{\sin B} = \dfrac{c}{\sin C}$
cosine rule $a^2 = b^2 + c^2 - 2bc \cos A$
area of triangle = $\frac{1}{2} ab \sin C$

Quadratic equations
The solutions of $ax^2 + bx + c = 0$, where $a \neq 0$,
Are given by $x = \dfrac{-b \pm \sqrt{b^2 - 4ac}}{2a}$

Talk about the test

Look at the test you have recently taken, and then answer the questions.

Test: _____   Score: _____ / _____

How did you feel about the test? Tick one.

☐ confident

☐ a little unsure

☐ not confident at all

Which questions did you find easiest, and why?

_____

_____

_____

_____

_____

Which questions did you find hardest, and why?

_____

_____

_____

_____

What could you do differently next time you take a test?

_____

_____

_____

_____

_____

MATHS HIGHER

Edexcel

Further support for parents

Test: _____   **Score:** _____ / _____

The areas assessed in the test were…

_____

_____

_____

Areas of success were…

_____

_____

_____

Areas for improvement were…

_____

_____

_____

Ideas for further practice include…

_____

_____

_____

You could support your child by…

_____

_____

_____

MATHS HIGHER

Topic tests

How to use

The following pages contain 38 topic tests designed to check the student's progress after each of the 38 lessons contained in the Tutor Delivery pack.

Each topic test can be used in a number of ways:

- as a diagnostic test
- as a homework activity
- as a main activity if extra time is available
- as revision closer to the tests.

Each test is worth 10 marks and should take 20 minutes to complete. The questions are more informal than the subsequent checkpoint challenges (pages 50–77) and practice papers (pages 78–111).

For questions marked with a pencil icon, it is important for the student to show their working in the space provided.

Some questions may require extra paper for working or for constructing diagrams and graphs.

MATHS HIGHER

1 Diagnostic lesson (topic test)

1. Given that x and y are positive integers, find all of the values of x and y that satisfy the equation $2x + 3y = 14$.

_____ **1 mark**

2. When $b = 3$, $5a + 2b = 16$. Work out the value of a when $b = 3$.

_____ **2 marks**

3. Marcus has tried to work out the answer to 234×23 but he has made some mistakes.

Identify his mistakes and correct his work.

```
        2   3   4
  ×         2   3
        7   0   2
          1   1
  +   4  6   8   0
      5  3   8   2
         1
```

3 marks

4. Given that $246 \times 84 = 20\,664$, work out the following:

a) 24.6×8.4 _____ **1 mark**

b) 2460×0.84 _____ **1 mark**

c) $20\,664 \div 840$ _____ **1 mark**

5. Which of these shapes is the odd one out? Give your reasons. There are several different answers!

A:  B: 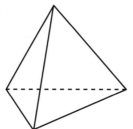 C: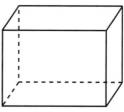

_____

_____ **1 mark**

MATHS HIGHER

Edexcel

2 Number: Standard form (topic test)

1. Write these numbers in standard form.

   a) 23 000 _____ **1 mark**

   b) 0.000 045 _____ **1 mark**

2. Write these numbers in order, from smallest to largest.

   3^0　　　　　10^{-3}　　　　　0.1×10^2　　　　　3×10^{-2}　　　　　**2 marks**

   _____　　_____　　　_____　　　　_____

3. Write the number $\sqrt{4\,000\,000}$ in standard form.

   _____ **2 marks**

4. Work out the value of $(4 \times 10^2) \times (6 \times 10^4)$. Do not use a calculator. Write your answer in standard form.

   _____

   _____ **1 mark**

5. Work out $(4 \times 10^{-3}) + (2.3 \times 10^{-4})$. Write your answer in standard form.

   _____ **1 mark**

6. Jupiter has a mass of 1.9×10^{27} kg. Earth has a mass of 6×10^{24} kg.

   How many times more massive is Jupiter than Earth?

   Give your answer to the nearest whole number.

   _____

   _____ **2 marks**

13

3 Number: Surds (topic test)

1. Simplify these values fully. Do not use a calculator.

   a) $\sqrt{112}$ _____ 1 mark

   b) $\sqrt{75}$ _____ 1 mark

   c) $\sqrt{20} + \sqrt{80}$ _____ 1 mark

   d) $\dfrac{\sqrt{20}}{\sqrt{5}}$ _____ 1 mark

2. Write $\dfrac{1}{\sqrt[3]{5}}$ as a single power of 5.

   _____ 1 mark

3. Expand and simplify $(2 + \sqrt{3})(3 - \sqrt{3})$. Do not use a calculator.

   _____

   _____ 2 marks

4. Rationalise the denominator of $\dfrac{6}{\sqrt{3}}$. Write your answer in its simplest form.

   _____ 1 mark

5. Show that $\dfrac{(1 + \sqrt{2})}{(3 - \sqrt{2})} = \dfrac{1}{7}(5 + 4\sqrt{2})$.

   _____

   _____ 2 marks

Edexcel

4 Number: Roots and indices (topic test)

 1. Draw lines to match the equivalent values.

$(-1)^4$		$9^{\frac{1}{2}}$
$\sqrt[3]{27}$		2^3
$64^{\frac{1}{2}}$		5^0

2 marks

 2. Find the reciprocal of 0.2.

_____ **1 mark**

 3. Work out the exact value of $\dfrac{4^3 \times 5^{-1}}{5^{-3} \times 4^2}$. Do not use a calculator.

_____

_____

_____ **2 marks**

 4. Find the value of each of these expressions. Do not use a calculator.

a) $27^{\frac{2}{3}}$ _____ **1 mark**

b) $\left(\dfrac{27}{125}\right)^{\frac{-2}{3}}$ _____ **2 marks**

 5. Write $256^{\frac{1}{2}}$ as a power of 2.

_____

_____ **2 marks**

5 Number: Factors and multiples (topic test)

1. What is 126 written as a product of its prime factors? Circle your answer.

    $1 \times 2 \times 3 \times 3 \times 7$ $2 \times 9 \times 7$ $2 \times 3 \times 3 \times 7$ 6×21

    1 mark

2. Write 1050 as a product of its prime factors.

    _____

    _____

    2 marks

3. Find the highest common factor of 882 and 1050.

    _____

    _____

    2 marks

4. Sarah wants to put lunchboxes together for a party. Each lunchbox will contain one bag of crisps, one drink and one chocolate bar.

    Bags of crisps come in packs of 12.

    Cans of drink come in packs of 10.

    Chocolate bars come in packs of 6.

    Sarah wants an equal number of crisps, drinks and chocolate bars and needs enough for at least 40 boxes. How many packs of each item does she need to buy?

    _____

    _____

    2 marks

5. Given that $120 = 2^3 \times 3 \times 5$, write the following as products of their prime factors. Use indices in your answers.

    a) 360   _____   **1 mark**

    b) 14 400   _____   **2 marks**

6 Number: Calculations (topic test)

1. Work out the answer to each of these calculations. Give your answers as mixed numbers.

    a) $2\frac{2}{3} + 1\frac{4}{5}$ _____   1 mark

    b) $3\frac{1}{4} \times 1\frac{1}{2}$ _____   1 mark

2. Mark has a piece of wood $2\frac{1}{3}$ m long. He cuts it into $\frac{3}{4}$ m long pieces.

    How many whole pieces of wood can he cut?

    _____

    _____

    _____   2 marks

3. Work out $\frac{\pi}{4} - \frac{\pi}{5}$. Give your answer in its exact form.

    _____   1 mark

4. Work out an estimate for each of these surd calculations. Give your answers to the nearest whole number.

    a) $\sqrt{103}$ _____   1 mark

    b) $\sqrt{79} \times \sqrt{5}$ _____   1 mark

    c) $\sqrt{143} + \sqrt{27}$ _____   1 mark

5. $7056 = 2^4 \times 3^2 \times 7^2$

    a) Write $\sqrt{7056}$ as a product of its prime factors.

    _____   1 mark

    b) Write $70\,560$ as a product of its prime factors.

    _____   1 mark

MATHS HIGHER

7 Number: Percentages and fractions (topic test)

1. Write 0.5% as a fraction in its simplest form.

    _____ **1 mark**

2. How would you increase 120 g by 2.5%? Circle the correct calculation.

    120×2.5 120×0.025 120×1.25 120×1.025

    1 mark

3. After a 12% decrease in price, the cost of a television is £281.60.

    Work out the original price of the television.

    _____

    _____ **2 marks**

4. A car hire company will increase the price of its hire by 5% each year for the next four years.

    The cost of hiring a car in 2017 is £130. How much will it be in 2021?

    _____

    _____ **2 marks**

5. The price of property increased 14% in 2016. It then fell 8% in 2017.

    Paul says this was a percentage increase of 6% over two years.

    Paul is incorrect. Use calculations to show the actual percentage increase.

    Give your answer to the nearest percent.

    _____

    _____ **2 marks**

6. A car depreciates in value at a rate of 15% per annum.

    If it is worth £18 423.75 in 2017, how much was it worth in 2014?

    _____

    _____ **2 marks**

8 Number: Rounding and estimation (topic test)

1. A plank of wood is 4.8 m long to 2 significant figures.

Complete the error interval for the measurement.

_____

_____

_____ < length ≤ _____   **2 marks**

2. Write 0.1̇4̇ as a fraction.

_____   **2 marks**

3. The length of a square is measured as 2.34 cm to 2 decimal places.

Calculate the error interval for the area of the square.

_____

_____

_____

_____ < area ≤ _____   **3 marks**

4. An athlete runs 800 metres at an average speed of 6.5 m/s.

The distance is accurate to the nearest metre and the speed is accurate to the nearest 0.1 m/s.

Calculate the maximum and minimum time that she took to run the 800 m. Give your answer to an appropriate degree of accuracy.

_____

_____

_____   **3 marks**

9 Algebra: Introducing algebra (topic test)

1. Use the equation $y = x^2 - 5$ to answer the following questions.

   a) When $y = 44$, find the two possible values of x.

   _____ **1 mark**

   b) Rearrange the formula to make x the subject.

   _____ **1 mark**

2. Expand and simplify $(2x + 3)(x - 2)$.

   _____ **1 mark**

3. Show that $(x + 1)(x - 2)(x + 4) \equiv x^3 + 3x^2 - 6x - 8$.

   _____ **2 marks**

4. Use the functions $f(x) = 3x + 1$ and $g(x) = x^2$ to answer the following questions.

   a) Work out $f(2)$.

   _____ **1 mark**

   b) Write an expression for $fg(x)$.

   _____ **1 mark**

   c) Write an expression for $gf(x)$.

   _____ **1 mark**

   d) Write an expression for $f^{-1}(x)$

   _____ **2 marks**

10 Algebra: Solving linear equations (topic test)

 1. Abby is four years older than Aziz. Aziz is twice as old as Chris.

The sum of all three of their ages is 109 years. Work out how old Chris is.

_____   _____ **1 mark**

2. Solve these equations.

 a) $4x + 5 = 2x - 7$

_____ **1 mark**

 b) $3(2x + 4) = 3x - 8$

_____ **1 mark**

 c) $3x^2 = x^2 + 72$

_____ **1 mark**

 d) $\dfrac{x + 5}{3} = \dfrac{2(x + 3)}{4}$

_____ **1 mark**

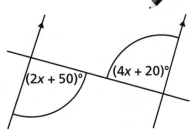 **3.** A line crosses a pair of parallel lines at the angles given.

Work out the value of x.

_____

_____

_____ **2 marks**

 4. The area of this shape is $110\,\text{cm}^2$.

Find the perimeter of the shape.

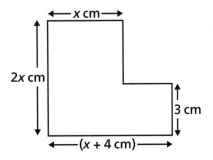

_____

_____

_____ **3 marks**

11 Algebra: Solving quadratic equations (topic test)

1. Write the solutions to each of these equations.

a) $(x + 3)(x - 4) = 0$

_____ **1 mark**

b) $(2x + 1)(3x - 5) = 0$

_____ **1 mark**

2. Use factorisation to solve each of these quadratic equations.

a) $x^2 - 4x - 12 = 0$

_____

_____ **2 marks**

b) $2x^2 + x - 3 = 0$

_____

_____ **2 marks**

3. Complete the square to solve $x^2 + 2x - 7 = 0$.

Leave your answer in surd form.

_____

_____

_____ **2 marks**

4. Use the quadratic formula to solve $3x^2 + 5x - 2 = 0$.

_____

_____

_____ **2 marks**

Edexcel

12 Algebra: Simultaneous equations (topic test)

 1. Solve these simultaneous equations algebraically.

a) $3x + y = 10$ $\qquad$ $6x - y = 8$

_____

_____

$x =$ _____ $\qquad$ $y =$ _____ **2 marks**

b) $3a + 4b = 17$ $\qquad$ $6b = 8 - a$

_____

_____

$a =$ _____ $\qquad$ $b =$ _____ **2 marks**

 2. A museum exhibition charges different prices for adult tickets and child tickets.

The cost of 3 adult tickets and 4 child tickets is £137.

The cost of 2 adult tickets and 3 child tickets is £96.50.

Find the price of an adult ticket and the price of a child ticket.

_____

_____

_____ **3 marks**

 3. On the same set of axes, sketch the graphs of $y = x^2 + 1$ and $y = x + 3$.

Find the solutions to the simultaneous equations $y = x^2 + 1$ and $y = x + 3$.

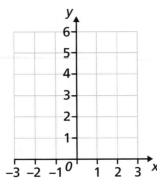

_____

_____

_____

$x =$ _____ $\qquad$ $y =$ _____ **3 marks**

23

13 Algebra: Iteration (topic test)

1. Using $x_{n+1} = 4 + \dfrac{5}{x_n^2}$ and $x_0 = 3.5$, find the exact values of x_1, x_2 and x_3.

_____

_____

_____ **3 marks**

2. The equation $x^3 + 3x = 7$ has a solution between $x = 1$ and $x = 2$.

a) Show that this is true.

_____

_____ **2 marks**

b) Show that $x^3 + 3x = 7$ can be rearranged to give $x = \dfrac{7}{x^2 + 3}$.

_____

_____ **2 marks**

c) Starting with $x_0 = 1$, use the iterative formula $x_{n+1} = \dfrac{7}{x_n^2 + 3}$ to find the solution to $x^3 + 3x = 7$.

Give your answer to 2 decimal places.

_____

_____

_____ **3 marks**

MATHS HIGHER

14 Algebra: Inequalities (topic test)

 1. Write the integer solutions to the inequality $-3 < x \leqslant 1$.

_____ 1 mark

 2. Write the inequality that is represented on this number line.

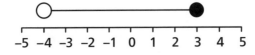

_____ 1 mark

 3. Solve the inequality $3a - 5 \geqslant -20$.

_____ 1 mark

 4. Write all the integers that satisfy $2x \geqslant -4$ and $3x < 9$.

_____

_____ 2 marks

 5. List the integer values of n that satisfy the inequality $-5 \leqslant 2n + 1 < 9$.

_____ 1 mark

 6. Solve the inequality $7x - 3 \leqslant 4x + 15$.

_____

_____ 2 marks

 7. Solve the inequality $x^2 - x - 6 < 0$. Sketch a graph on a separate piece of paper to help.

_____

_____ 2 marks

15 Algebra: Sequences (topic test)

1. Label each of these sequences arithmetic, geometric or quadratic.

   A: 4, 8, 16, 32, 64, 128…   _____

   B: 3, 8, 15, 24, 35, 48…   _____

   C: 7, 11, 15, 19, 23, 27…   _____   **2 marks**

2. Find the nth term of each of the sequences in question 1.

   A: _____

   _____

   B: _____

   _____

   C: _____

   _____   **6 marks**

3. The general term of a sequence is $2n^2 - 10$.

   How many terms of the sequence will have a value that is less than 50?

   _____

   _____   **2 marks**

16 Algebra: Linear, quadratic, cubic and reciprocal graphs (topic test)

1. Here are the equations of four straight lines.

A	B	C	D
$y = 4x - 2$	$2y = -4x + 5$	$2y - 8x = 3$	$2y - x = 1$

 a) Which graphs are parallel to one another?

_____ **1 mark**

 b) Which graphs are perpendicular to one another?

_____ **1 mark**

 2. Find the equation of the straight line that passes through the points (2, 11) and (5, 23).

_____

_____ **2 marks**

 3. Find the equation of the straight line that is perpendicular to $2y = 4x + 3$ and passes through the point (4, 8).

_____

_____ **2 marks**

 4. A graph has the equation $y = x^2 + 8x + 12$.

a) Complete the table, finding the values of $y = x^2 + 8x + 12$ for $x = -8$ to $x = 0$.

x	-8	-7	-6	-5	-4	-3	-2	-1	0
y									

1 mark

b) On a sheet of graph paper, sketch the graph of $y = x^2 + 8x + 12$ for $x = -8$ to $x = 0$. **1 mark**

c) What are the coordinates of the points where the graph crosses the x-axis?

_____ **1 mark**

d) What are the coordinates of the turning point?

_____ **1 mark**

17 Algebra: Interpreting graphs (topic test)

1. This graph shows a journey Michael took in his car.

   a) What is the total distance Michael travelled?

   _____ **1 mark**

   b) How long was Michael stopped for in total?

   _____ **1 mark**

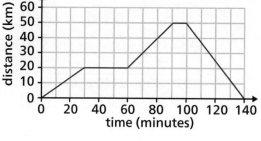

   c) Work out Michael's speed for the first 30 minutes of his journey. Give your answer in kilometres per hour.

   _____ **1 mark**

   d) When was Michael travelling fastest? Explain how you know.

   _____ **1 mark**

   e) Work out Michael's fastest speed in kilometres per hour.

   _____ **1 mark**

2. Here is a velocity–time graph.

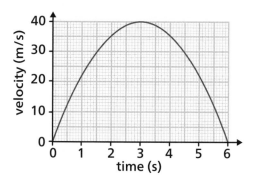

   a) Estimate the acceleration when $t = 1$ second.

   _____

   _____ **2 marks**

   b) At what time was the acceleration zero?
      Explain how you know.

   _____

   _____ **1 mark**

   c) Work out the distance travelled in the first 2 seconds.

   _____

   _____ **2 marks**

TUTORS GUILD MATHS HIGHER

18 Algebra: Trigonometric graphs and transformations (topic test)

1. Label these graphs either $\sin x$, $\cos x$ or $\tan x$.

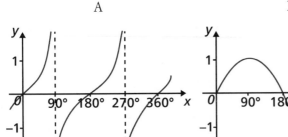 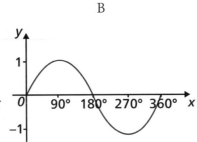 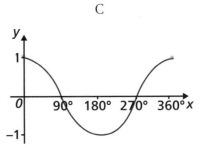

_____   _____   _____   **2 marks**

2. Joe said that the graph of $\sin(x + 90)$ looks the same as $\cos x$.

Is he correct? Give your reasons.

_____   **1 mark**

3. Here is the graph of $y = f(x)$. On the same set of axes sketch the following graphs.

a) $y = f(x) + 2$ _____ **1 mark**

b) $y = f(x - 2)$ _____ **1 mark**

c) $y = f(-x)$ _____ **1 mark**

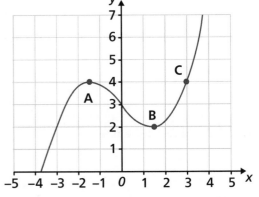

4. Describe what happens to the graph of $y = f(x)$ during the following translations.

a) $y = -f(x)$

_____   **1 mark**

b) $y = f(x + 4)$

_____   **1 mark**

5. The graph of $f(x)$ has a turning point at $(-3, 7)$.

Write the new coordinates of this point for the graph $-f(x) - 5$.

_____

_____   **2 marks**

19 Algebra: Graphs of circles (topic test)

1. A circle has the equation $x^2 + y^2 = 25$.

    a) Write the coordinates of the centre of the circle.

    _____ **1 mark**

    b) What is the radius of the circle?

    _____ **1 mark**

    c) Circle any points which lie on the circumference of the circle.

    $(1, 2)$ $(2, 3)$ $(3, 4)$ $(4, 5)$ **1 mark**

2. Write the equation of a circle with:

    a) radius 3 cm and centre $(0, 0)$

    _____ **1 mark**

    b) diameter 12 cm and centre $(0, 0)$.

    _____ **1 mark**

3. A circle has the equation $x^2 + y^2 = 4$.

    Sketch the circle on the axes.

    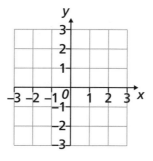

    2 marks

4. The point $(3, 1)$ lies on the circumference of the circle $x^2 + y^2 = 10$.

    a) Find the gradient of the line that joins the centre of the circle to point $(3, 1)$.

    _____ **1 mark**

    b) Find the equation of the tangent to the circle at point $(3, 1)$.

    _____ **2 marks**

    30

MATHS HIGHER

20 Ratio, proportion and rates of change: Ratio (topic test)

1. A triangle has angles in the ratio $5:4:3$.

   What is the size of the largest angle?

   _____

   _____ **2 marks**

2. There are one third as many adults as children at a theme park. Write the ratio of adults to children.

   _____

   _____ **2 marks**

3. Red to white paint is mixed in the ratio $3:7$.

   Write the ratio in the form $1:n$.

   _____ **1 mark**

4. 320 people watch a theatre show.

   The ratio of men to women is $4:1$.

   How many more men than women watch the show?

   _____

   _____ **2 marks**

5. The ratio of lions to tigers in a zoo is $2:3$.

   Write an equation for the number of tigers (t) relative to the number of lions (l).

   _____ **1 mark**

6. Aisha, Khalil and Claire share some money in the ratio $1 : 3\frac{1}{2} : 6\frac{1}{2}$.

   Claire gets £48 more than Khalil.

   What was the total amount of money they shared between them?

   _____

   _____ **2 marks**

21 Ratio, proportion and rates of change: Bearings and scale (topic test)

1. The scale on a map is $1:300\,000$.

   a) What would 4 cm on the map represent in kilometres?

_____ **1 mark**

   b) The actual distance between two towns is 15 km. What would this distance be on the map?

_____ **1 mark**

2. Complete this sentence.

The loci of points 6 cm from a fixed point is a _____ with _____ 6 cm. **1 mark**

3. Look at this scale drawing of two points labelled A and B.   **B**x

   Scale = $1:200\,000$

   a) Work out the actual distance and bearing of A from B.

_____   **N**↑   **2 marks**
                                                 Ax

   b) C is 5 km from A. The bearing of C from A is 120°.

     Mark point C on the diagram. **1 mark**

4. Draw the loci of the set of points 1 cm from this line.

_____

2 marks

5. The bearing of a ship from a lighthouse is 100°. Work out the bearing of the lighthouse from the ship.

_____

_____ **2 marks**

32

22 Ratio, proportion and rates of change: Direct and inverse proportion (topic test)

1. Look at this table of values for x and y.

x	1	4	7	10
y	4.5	6	7.5	9

     a) On a sheet of graph paper, plot a graph of x against y.   **1 mark**

     b) Does your graph show direct proportion? Explain your answer.

_____ **1 mark**

2. It takes two students 30 minutes to sharpen a box of pencils. Work out how long the same task will take:

    a) one student   _____   **1 mark**

    b) six students.   _____   **1 mark**

3. A bank offers an exchange rate of 1 GBP (£) = 1.13 euros (€).

    a) Work out how many euros you would get for £400.

_____ **1 mark**

    b) How many GBP would you get for €200? Give your answer to the nearest penny.

_____ **1 mark**

    c) A handbag in the UK costs £120. In Spain it costs €130. Is the handbag cheaper in the UK or in Spain?

_____ **1 mark**

    d) Write an equation that links pounds (P) to euros (E).

_____ **1 mark**

4. S is inversely proportional to T. When $S = 8$, $T = 5$.

     a) Find an equation that connects S and T.

_____ **1 mark**

     b) Find the value of S when $T = 4$.

_____ **1 mark**

23 Ratio, proportion and rates of change: Rates of change (topic test)

1. A business aims to increase sales by 15% each month.

    In January, the business made 400 sales.

    How many sales should it make in May to reach its target?

    _____

    _____ **2 marks**

2. The value of a motorhome depreciates by 8% per annum.

    The original price of the motorhome is £80 000.

    a) Form an equation showing the value, v, after t years.

    _____ **1 mark**

    b) How much will the motorhome be worth after 5 years?

    _____ **1 mark**

    c) After how many years will the motorhome be worth less than £30 000?

    _____

    _____ **2 marks**

3. The iterative formula $p_{t+1} = 1.07p_t$ is used to calculate the projected price, p, of a property over t years.

    a) What percentage could be used to calculate the annual increase?

    _____ **1 mark**

    b) If $p_0 = £120 000$, work out the value of p_1, p_2 and p_3.

    _____

    _____

    _____ **3 marks**

24 Geometry and measures: Angles (topic test)

1. The bearing of A from B is 070°. Work out the bearing of B from A.

_____

_____ **2 marks**

2. Find the number of sides on each of these shapes.

a) A regular polygon with a 15° exterior angle.

_____ **1 mark**

b) A regular polygon with a 135° interior angle.

_____ **1 mark**

3. Find the size of an interior angle in a 12-sided regular polygon.

_____ **1 mark**

4. The interior angle of a regular polygon is $5x°$. The exterior angle is $x°$.

How many sides does the polygon have?

_____

_____ **2 marks**

5. The diagram shows a regular hexagon and two equilateral triangles.

Work out the size of angle x.

_____

_____ **3 marks**

35

MATHS HIGHER

Edexcel

25 Geometry and measures: 2-D shapes (topic test)

1. Match each quadrilateral to its description. Some descriptions could match more than one shape.

    Make sure you choose the right one!

rectangle	Opposite sides are parallel and equal in length. Diagonals bisect one another. Opposite angles are equal.
parallelogram	Only two sides are parallel.
kite	A parallelogram with all sides equal in length.
rhombus	Opposite sides are parallel and equal in length. All angles are right angles.
trapezium	Two pairs of adjacent sides are equal. Shorter diagonal is bisected by the longer diagonal at right angles. One pair of opposite angles are equal.

4 marks

2. Construct the perpendicular bisector of line AB.

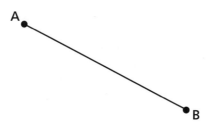

1 mark

3. Bisect this angle using a pair of compasses and a straight edge.

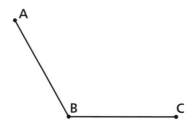

2 marks

4. Here is a plan of a garden. Sean wants to plant a tree less than 6 m from A and closer to CD than AB.

    Shade the area in which the tree could be planted.

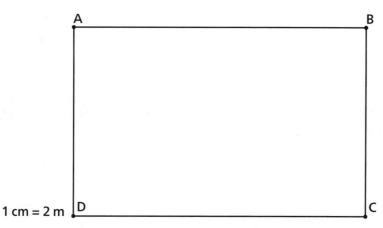

1 cm = 2 m

3 marks

TUTORS GUILD **MATHS** HIGHER

26 Geometry and measures: Perimeter, area and volume (topic test)

1. Work out the area of this shape.

   _____

   _____

   1 mark

2. The area of this triangle is 15 cm². Work out the height of the triangle.

   _____

   _____

   1 mark

3. Work out the perimeter of this semicircle.

   Give your answer to 3 significant figures.

   _____

   _____

   2 marks

4. Work out the surface area of this triangular prism.

   _____

   _____

   2 marks

5. Work out the volume of this cylinder. Give your answer to 3 significant figures.

   _____

   _____

   2 marks

6. Given that the volume of a cone $= \frac{1}{3}\pi r^2 h$, work out the volume of this cone.
   Give your answer to 3 significant figures.

   _____

   _____

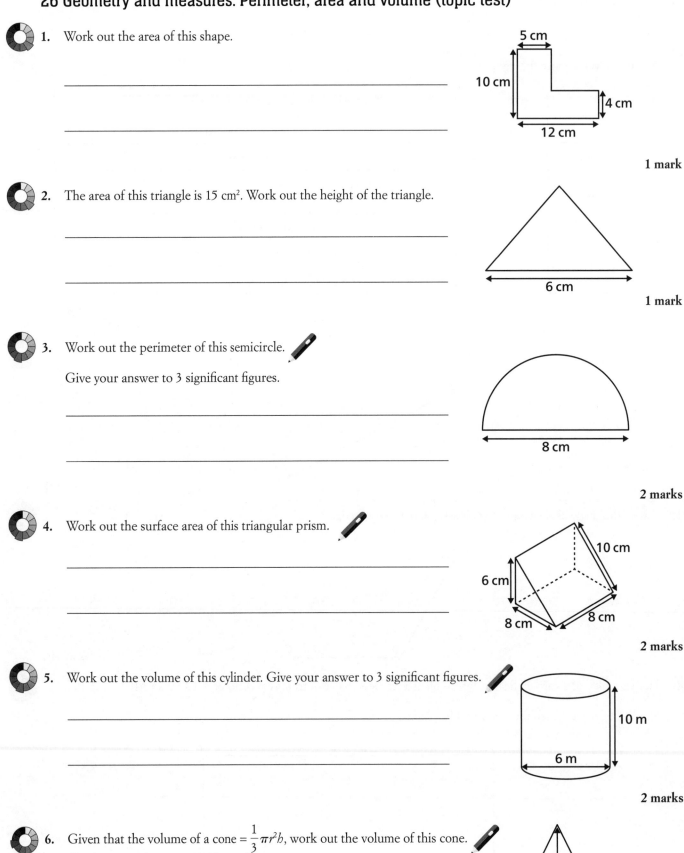
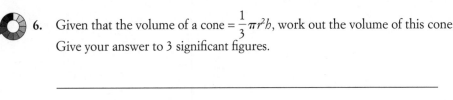

2 marks

27 Geometry and measures: Pythagoras' theorem (topic test)

1. Use Pythagoras' theorem to work out which sets of lengths belong to right-angled triangles.
   Circle your answers.

   10 cm, 11 cm, 12 cm   10 cm, 24 cm, 26 cm   10 cm, 12 cm, 14 cm   12 cm, 16 cm, 20 cm   **1 mark**

2. Work out the length of the diagonal in a square with 5 cm long sides. Give your answer to 3 significant figures.

   _____

   _____   **2 marks**

3. Find the distance between the coordinates (2, 4) and (8, 7). Give your answer to 3 significant figures.

   _____

   _____   **2 marks**

4. Work out the height of this isosceles triangle. Give your answer to 3 significant figures.

   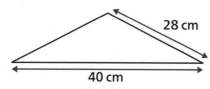

   28 cm

   40 cm

   _____

   _____   **2 marks**

5. A cuboid has dimensions 7 cm by 6 cm by 5 cm.

   Find the length of the diagonal, x. Give your answer to 3 significant figures.

   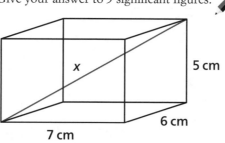

   x 5 cm

   6 cm

   7 cm

   _____

   _____   **3 marks**

28 Geometry and measures: Using trigonometry (topic test)

 1. The diagram shows the sloping edge of a roof. Work out the angle between the roof and the horizontal.

Give your answer to 3 significant figures.

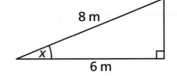

_____

_____ **1 mark**

 2. Work out the area of this isosceles triangle. Give your answer to 3 significant figures.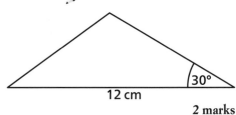

_____

_____

2 marks

 3. The diagram shows a quadrilateral. Work out the value of angle x.

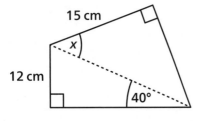

_____

_____

_____ **2 marks**

 4. A plane leaves an airport on a bearing of 150° for 20 km. How far east has the plane travelled?

_____

_____ **2 marks**

5. The diagram shows a cuboid.

 a) Show that the angle GAC is 45°.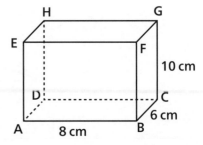

_____

_____ **2 marks**

 b) Work out the length of the diagonal GA.

Give your answer to 3 significant figures.

_____ **1 mark**

29 Geometry and measures: Trigonometric values (topic test)

1. Write the exact values of these trigonometric ratios. The first one has been done for you.

$\sin 45$	$\dfrac{1}{\sqrt{2}}$
$\cos 30$	
$\sin 90$	
$\tan 30$	
$\cos 90$	

3 marks

2. Find the length of side x in this triangle. Give your answer to 3 significant figures.

_____

_____ **2 marks**

3. Find the value of angle a in this triangle. Give your answer to 3 significant figures.

_____

_____ **2 marks**

4. Find the length of side BC in this triangle. Give your answer to 3 significant figures.

_____

_____ **2 marks**

5. Work out the area of this triangle.

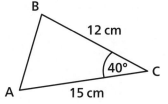

_____

_____ **1 mark**

40

30 Geometry and measures: Circles (topic test)

1. Work out the area of this sector.

_____

_____

_____

9 cm

70°

1 mark

2. What is the angle of a sector with radius 5 cm and arc length 6.3 cm?

Give your answer to the nearest whole number.

_____

_____ **1 mark**

3. A sector has an area of 20 cm² and an angle of 30°.

Work out the arc length of the sector.

Give your answer in cm to 1 decimal place.

_____

_____ **2 marks**

4. Work out the value of angle x. Give reasons for your working.

_____

_____

_____

120°

x

3 marks

5. Work out the value of angles x and y in this circle. Give reasons for your working.

72°

y

x

_____

_____

_____ **3 marks**

31 Geometry and measures: Vectors (topic test)

1. Two vectors are given as $\vec{OA} = \begin{pmatrix} 2 \\ 1 \end{pmatrix}$, $\vec{AB} = \begin{pmatrix} 2 \\ -4 \end{pmatrix}$.

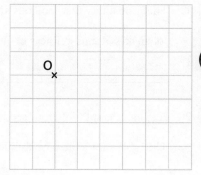

a) Draw the line segments that represent each of these vectors.

 2 marks

b) Write $\vec{OB}$ as a column vector.

_____ **1 mark**

c) Draw the line segment that represents the vector $\vec{OB}$.

1 mark

d) Work out the magnitude of $\vec{OB}$.

_____ **1 mark**

2. Work out the following where $\mathbf{a} = \begin{pmatrix} 5 \\ 3 \end{pmatrix}$ and $\mathbf{b} = \begin{pmatrix} -1 \\ -2 \end{pmatrix}$.

a) $\mathbf{a} - \mathbf{b}$ _____ **1 mark**

b) $2\mathbf{a} + 3\mathbf{b}$ _____ **1 mark**

3. X is the mid-point of $\vec{CA}$ and Y is the mid-point of $\vec{CB}$ where $\vec{CA} = \mathbf{a}$ and $\vec{CB} = \mathbf{b}$.
Show that the vector $\vec{XY}$ is parallel to $\vec{AB}$.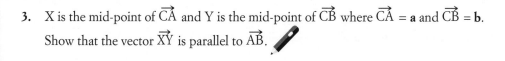

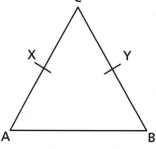

_____

_____

_____ **3 marks**

32 Probability: Basic probability and Venn diagrams (topic test)

 1. The probability that Joe's bus arrives on time is 0.8.

Joe makes 50 bus journeys in one month. How many times should he expect the bus to not be on time?

_____ **1 mark**

 2. A spinner is split into four sections coloured either red, green, yellow or white.

The table shows the probabilities of the spinner landing on each colour.

Colour	red	green	yellow	blue
Probability	$3x$	$2x + 0.1$	$2x - 0.1$	$3x + 0.2$

a) Work out the probability of the spinner landing on yellow.

_____ **2 marks**

b) The spinner is spun 200 times. How many times would you expect it to land on blue?

_____ **1 mark**

 3. A physics class, a biology class and a chemistry class each have 20 students.

Some students are in more than one class.

4 students study biology, chemistry and physics.

10 students study biology and chemistry.

11 students study biology and physics.

9 students study chemistry and physics.

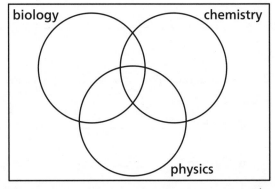

a) Complete the Venn diagram. **3 marks**

b) What is the probability that a student chosen at random only studies physics?

_____ **1 mark**

 4. This Venn diagram shows a set of numbers.

A is a set of prime numbers less than 10.

B is a set of multiples of 3 less than 10.

a) List all of the numbers in set A'.

_____ **1 mark**

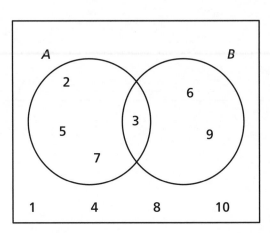

b) Joel chooses a number between 1 and 10 at random.

Find the probability that this number will be in set $A \cap B$.

_____ **1 mark**

Edexcel

33 Probability: Combined probability (topic test)

1. Mike chooses two numbers at random from the digits 1 to 5. He can choose the same number twice.

   a) Write the probability that the sum of the two numbers chosen is a two-digit number.

   _____ **1 mark**

   b) Work out the probability that the product of the two numbers chosen is a two-digit number.

   _____

   _____ **2 marks**

2. The probability that it rains on any one day during May is $\frac{1}{5}$.

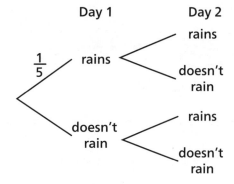

   a) Complete the tree diagram. **2 marks**

   b) Work out the probability that it rains on two consecutive days.

   _____ **1 mark**

   c) Work out the probability that, on three consecutive days, it rains on the first day, doesn't rain on the second day but rains on the third day.

   _____ **1 mark**

3. A biased coin is tossed twice. Given that the probability of it landing on heads twice is 0.36, work out the probability of it landing on tails twice.

   _____ **2 marks**

4. The probability that it will rain tomorrow is 0.6. The probability that Jenny will take an umbrella out with her tomorrow is 0.8.

   Bal thinks that the probability that it will rain and Jenny will take an umbrella out with her tomorrow is 0.48, because 0.6 × 0.8 = 0.48.

   What assumption has Bal made?

   _____ **1 mark**

34 Probability: Conditional probability (topic test)

1. A combination lock code requires three digits from 0 to 9.

All three digits must be different. For example, the code for the lock could be:

a) How many different combinations are there for the code of the lock?

_____ **1 mark**

b) Joe can remember the first two digits of his code, but not the third. What is the probability that he will guess the third digit correctly on his first attempt?

_____ **1 mark**

2. 25 students were asked if they travel to school by train or by bus.

16 students travel by train.

11 students travel by bus.

4 students don't travel by bus or train.

Some of the students take both the train and the bus.

a) On a separate sheet of paper draw a Venn diagram to represent this data. **3 marks**

b) A student is chosen at random. The student travels by train. Work out the probability that this student also travels by bus.

_____ **1 mark**

3. This two-way table shows the results of a survey about hair colour and eye colour in class A.

		Hair colour		
		Blonde	Brown	Ginger
Eye colour	Blue	6	3	2
	Green	5	8	4
	Brown	5	9	1

a) A student is chosen at random from class A. What is the probability that the student has brown hair and green eyes?

_____ **2 marks**

b) A student is chosen at random. Given that the student has ginger hair, what is the probability that they also have green eyes?

_____ **2 marks**

35 Statistics: Planning an investigation and data collection (topic test)

1. The manager of a sports centre designs this data collection sheet to find out how many people go to the gym in one month.

Number of people	0–100	100–200	200–400	400–500
Tally				

   a) State two problems with the tally chart.

   _____

   _____ **2 marks**

   b) On a separate sheet of paper, redesign the tally chart. **1 mark**

2. A marine biologist wants to find out the weights of baby dolphins three months after they are born.
   Which one of these best describes the type of data they are collecting? Circle your answer.

   A: primary, discrete   B: primary, continuous   C: secondary, discrete   D: secondary, continuous   **1 mark**

3. Simon wants to know the most popular mode of transport of people in his school.
   The school has 600 students. Explain, in detail, how he could take:

   a) a random sample

   _____

   _____ **2 marks**

   b) a stratified sample.

   _____

   _____ **2 marks**

4. A sports centre has 3000 members. Of these, 1600 people have a full membership and the rest have a part membership. The manager carries out a survey of 300 members to find out how satisfied they are with the facilities. He wants the sample to be representative of both membership types. How many part members should be included in the survey?

   _____

   _____ **2 marks**

MATHS HIGHER

36 Statistics: Constructing graphs, charts and diagrams (topic test)

1. This partially-completed stem-and-leaf diagram shows the marks received by Class B in a maths test.

    Class A sat the same test and received these marks:

32	33	44	35	50	62
47	57	75	42	69	72
45	80	33	51	63	53
81	46	57	61	72	

Class A		Class B			
	2	7	8		
	3	1	4	5	7
	4	2	2	4	6
	5	0	0	0	4 9
	6	2	3	5	7
	7	1	2		
	8	1	3		

    Key
    Class A: 1| 2 means 21 marks
    Class B: 1| 2 means 12 marks

 a) Complete the stem-and-leaf diagram for class A. **2 marks**

 b) Complete this table and use it to construct a dual bar chart for both classes' scores.

Marks	20–29	30–39	40–49	50–59	60–69	70–79	80–89
Class A frequency							
Class B frequency							

3 marks

 c) Write the advantages and disadvantages of displaying the data in a dual bar chart compared to a stem-and-leaf diagram.

_____ **1 mark**

 2. These charts show the genres of films watched by people at a cinema one weekend.

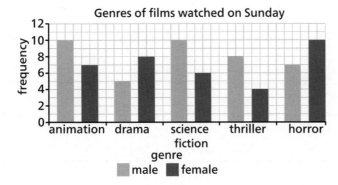

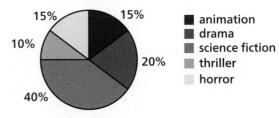

a) 'More people watched Science Fiction on Saturday than on Sunday'. Is this statement true or false?

Explain your reasons.

_____ **2 marks**

b) "A higher proportion of people watched an animation film on Sunday than on Saturday". Is this statement true or false?

Explain your reasons.

_____ **2 marks**

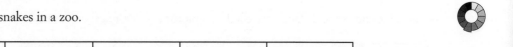

37 Statistics: Interpreting data (topic test)

1. This table shows the lengths of snakes in a zoo.

Length (cm)	$10 \leqslant a < 20$	$20 \leqslant a < 30$	$30 \leqslant a < 40$	$40 \leqslant a < 50$	$50 \leqslant a < 60$
Frequency	1	3	10	9	8

a) Which is the modal class?

_____ **1 mark**

b) Which class contains the median?

_____ **1 mark**

c) Work out an estimate for the mean length of snakes. Give your answer to 3 significant figures.

_____

_____ **3 marks**

2. Claire did an experiment where she recorded the length of time it took a group of 15 children to complete a puzzle. Here are the times, in seconds, it took each child to complete the puzzle.

23   23   24   24   26   28   28   30   32   32   34   37   37   38   38

a) Draw a box plot for this information.

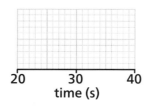

20   30   40
time (s)

3 marks

Three months later, Claire repeated the experiment with the same children.

The median time a month later is 25. The interquartile range is 8.

The range is 12.

b) Were the results of the experiment more consistent at the beginning or after three months?

Give a reason for your answer.

_____

_____ **2 marks**

38 Statistics: Scatter graphs, cumulative frequency graphs and histograms

 1. The table shows the distance travelled by a motor courier and the time taken for 12 journeys.

Distance (km)	10	14	12	15	17	5	8	10	12	15	10	8
Time (mins)	30	28	32	35	40	10	15	20	25	20	20	10

a) On a sheet of graph paper, plot a scatter graph to show this data.   **2 marks**

b) What type of correlation does the scatter graph show?

_____   **1 mark**

c) Another journey has a distance of 11 km. Use your scatter graph to show how long the journey might take.

_____   **2 marks**

 2. This cumulative frequency graph shows the heights (mm) of 60 saplings after 1 month.

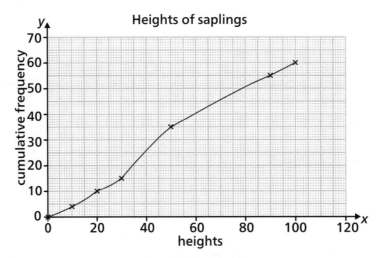

a) Work out the median height.

_____   **1 mark**

b) Work out the interquartile range.

_____   **1 mark**

c) On a sheet of graph paper, draw a histogram showing the heights of the plants.   **3 marks**

MATHS HIGHER

Checkpoint challenges

How to use

Each of these checkpoint challenges is intended to cover one of the main topic areas addressed in the 9–1 GCSE exams: number; algebra; ratio, proportion and rates of change; geometry and measures; probability; and statistics.

Each challenge can be used in a number of ways:

- as a diagnostic test
- as a homework activity
- as a main activity if extra time is available
- as revision closer to the tests
- at the end of the relevant section of the lesson plans.

These challenges are designed to provide informal test practice, in addition to the more formal practice papers on pages 78–111. Each is worth 30 marks and should take 30 minutes to complete. The questions all are exam-style and increase in difficulty throughout the challenge. Each checkpoint challenge begins with two worked examples.

For questions marked with a pencil, it is important for the student to show their working in the space provided.

Number checkpoint challenge

The number checkpoint challenge covers content from specification points 3.1.1 Structure and calculation; 3.1.2 Fractions, decimals and percentages; and 3.1.3 Measures and accuracy. This material is also covered in lessons 2–6 of the Delivery pack.

Answers can be found on pages 122–123.

Algebra checkpoint challenge

The algebra checkpoint challenge covers content from specification points 3.2.1 Notation, vocabulary and manipulation; 3.2.2 Graphs; 3.2.3 Solving equations and inequalities; and 3.2.4 Sequences. This material is also covered in lessons 7–14 of the Delivery pack.

Answers can be found on pages 123–124.

Ratio, proportion and rates of change checkpoint challenge

The ratio, proportion and rates of change checkpoint challenge covers content from specification point 3.3 Ratio proportion and rates of change. This material is also covered in lessons 15–17 of the Delivery pack.

Answers can be found on page 125–126.

Geometry and measures checkpoint challenge

The geometry and measures checkpoint challenge covers content from specification points 3.4.1 Properties and constructions; 3.4.2 Mensuration and calculation; and 3.4.3 Vectors. This material is also covered in lessons 18–31 of the Delivery pack.

Answers can be found on page 126–127.

Probability checkpoint challenge

The probability checkpoint challenge covers content from specification point 3.5 Probability. This material is also covered in lessons 32 and 33 of the Delivery pack.

Answers can be found on pages 127–128.

Statistics checkpoint challenge

The specification checkpoint challenge covers content from specification point 3.6 Statistics. This material is also covered in lessons 34–38 of the Delivery pack.

Answers can be found on pages 128–130.

Edexcel

MATHS HIGHER

Number checkpoint challenge

Worked example 1

Prove algebraically that the recurring decimal $0.1\dot{2}$ can be written as the fraction $\frac{11}{90}$.

$$\text{Let } x = 0.122222222...$$
$$100x = 12.222222222...$$
$$10x = 1.222222222...$$
$$100x - 10x = 11$$
$$90x = 11$$
$$x = \frac{11}{90}$$

Worked example 2

$a = 4.3$ rounded to 1 decimal place.

$b = 3.46$ rounded to 3 significant figures.

Write the upper bound of $\frac{a}{b}$.

The upper bound of a, 4.3, is 4.35.

The lower bound of b, 3.46, is 3.455.

The upper bound of $\frac{a}{b} = \frac{\text{upper bound}}{\text{lower bound}}$.

$$= \frac{4.35}{3.455}$$
$$= 1.259$$

---

 1.   Nina knits woollen hats to sell. She has six different colours of wool and can choose from four different patterns. Each hat is made from one colour of wool.

How many combinations of styles can Nina make?

_____   **2 marks**

 2.   Work out $2\frac{2}{5} + \frac{3}{4}$.

Give your answer as a mixed number in its simplest form.

_____

_____   **3 marks**

 3.   Work out $\dfrac{3 \times 10^4 + 5 \times 10^3}{2 \times 10^{-3}}$.

Give your answer in standard form.

_____

_____   **2 marks**

Number checkpoint challenge

4. The height of a plant increases from 8.2 cm to 12.6 cm in one month.

    Calculate the percentage increase in its height.

    Give your answer correct to 3 significant figures.

    _____

    _____

    _____ **2 marks**

5. Prove algebraically that the recurring decimal $0.2\dot{3}\dot{4}$ can be written as the fraction $\dfrac{116}{495}$.

    _____

    _____

    _____ **3 marks**

6. Given that $P = 2^3 \times 3^2 \times 5 \times 7$ and $Q = 2^2 \times 5^2 \times 7^2$, write the following as products of powers of their prime factors:

    a) the highest common factor (HCF) of P and Q

    _____ **1 mark**

    b) the lowest common multiple (LCM) of P and Q

    _____ **1 mark**

    c) $10Q$

    _____ **1 mark**

    d) $\dfrac{1}{4}P$

    _____ **1 mark**

Number checkpoint challenge

  7. Work out an estimate for $\sqrt{5.34^2 - 3.63 \times 2.12}$.

_____

_____

_____ **3 marks**

  8. Work out the area of this triangle.

Give your answer in cm² and in the form $a\sqrt{3}$.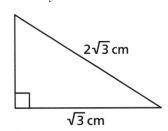

$2\sqrt{3}$ cm

$\sqrt{3}$ cm

_____

_____

_____ **3 marks**

9. The speed of an object can be found using the equation $S = \dfrac{D}{T}$, where S is speed, D is a given distance and T is a given time.

$D = 132.4$ km correct to 1 decimal place.

$T = 2$ hours correct to 1 significant figure.

Work out an upper bound for S in kilometres per hour.

_____

_____

_____ **3 marks**

Number checkpoint challenge

10. Find the values of these expressions.

   a) $\sqrt[3]{10^9 \times 3^6}$

   _____

   _____   **2 marks**

   b) $512^{\frac{-1}{3}}$

   _____

   _____   **1 mark**

11. $2^{3x} = \dfrac{1}{64}$. Solve for x.

   _____

   _____   **2 marks**

Total marks = 30

TUTORS' GUILD **MATHS** HIGHER

Algebra checkpoint challenge

Worked example 1:

Simplify $\dfrac{4a^5b^3}{2b^4}$.

$$= \frac{2a^5b^3}{b^4}$$

$$= 2a^5b^{-1}$$

Worked example 2:

Simplify $\dfrac{x+1}{2} + \dfrac{x-2}{3}$.

$$\frac{x+1}{2} + \frac{x-2}{3}$$

$$= \frac{3(x+1)}{6} + \frac{2(x-2)}{6}$$

$$= \frac{3x+3+2x-4}{6}$$

$$= \frac{5x-1}{6}$$

1. Simplify these expressions.

a) $(m^4)^{-2}$

_____ **1 mark**

b) $\dfrac{8p^3}{10p^5}$

_____ **1 mark**

2. Solve these equations.

a) $5^6 \times 5^x = 5^{10}$

_____ **1 mark**

b) $3y^3 = 192$

_____ **1 mark**

Edexcel

MATHS HIGHER

Algebra checkpoint challenge

3. Simplify $\dfrac{x+3}{4} + \dfrac{x+2}{5}$.

_____

_____

_____ **3 marks**

4. Given that a and b are integers when $(x+4)(x-2) + a + bx = x^2 + 5x - 10$, find the values of a and b.

_____

_____

_____ **3 marks**

5. The nth term of an arithmetic sequence is $3n + 5$, where n is a positive integer.

a) Is 259 a term of this sequence? Give a reason for your answer.

_____

_____ **2 marks**

b) Find an expression for the sum of the nth term and the $(n+1)^{\text{th}}$ term of this sequence. Give your answer in its simplest form.

_____

_____ **2 marks**

c) The sum of two consecutive terms in this sequence is 85. Find the smaller of these two terms.

_____

_____ **2 marks**

Algebra checkpoint challenge

 6. An iterative formula is given as $x_{n+1} = \sqrt{4 + \dfrac{2}{x_n}}$.

a) Use $x_{n+1} = \sqrt{4 + \dfrac{2}{x_n}}$ and $x_0 = 1$ to find the exact values of x_1, x_2 and x_3.

_____

_____

_____ **3 marks**

b) Explain what the values of x_1, x_2 and x_3 represent.

_____

_____ **1 mark**

 7. On the grid below, shade the region defined by these inequalities:

$$x + y < 5 \qquad\qquad x > -2 \qquad\qquad y > 1$$

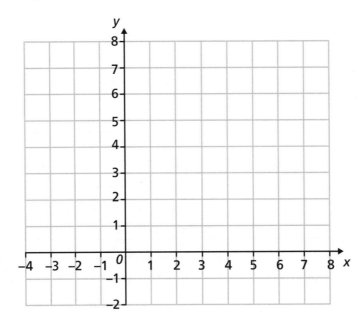

4 marks

Algebra checkpoint challenge

8. The functions f and g are such that $f(x) = 3 + 2x$ and $g(x) = 3x + 1$.

   a) Show that $gf(2) = 22$.

   _____

   _____ **2 marks**

   b) Find $f^{-1}(x)$.

   _____ **1 mark**

9. Expand and simplify $(4x - 1)(2x + 1)(3x + 2)$.

   _____

   _____

   _____ **3 marks**

Total marks = 30

Ratio and proportion checkpoint challenge

Worked example 1

Mike, Pablo and Simon shared some money in the ratio $4:8:5$.

Pablo got £15 more than Simon. How much money did Mike get?

$M:P:S = 4:8:5$

$8 - 5 = 3$: Pablo has three more parts than Simon.

3 parts $= £15$

1 part $= £5$

Mike has four parts: $4 \times £5 = £20$

Worked example 2

The ratio of $x:y = 4:7$. Write an equation connecting x and y.

$\dfrac{x}{y} = \dfrac{4}{7}$

$7x = 4y$ or $y = \dfrac{7}{4}x$.

1. Jamal, Claire and Peter shared some money in the ratio $3:5:9$.

   Peter got £60 more than Claire.

   How much money did Jamal get?

   _____

   _____

   _____   **3 marks**

2. In a shop, the number of apples and the number of pears are in the ratio $5:3$.

   The number of pears and the number of oranges are in the ratio $4:5$.

   The total number of apples, pears and oranges in the shop is 235.

   How many apples are there in the shop?

   _____

   _____

   _____   **3 marks**

Ratio and proportion checkpoint challenge

3. 12 bags of crisps have a total mass of 360 g.

Crisps have 550 calories per 100 g.

Work out the number of calories per bag of crisps.

_____

_____

_____   **3 marks**

4. The four graphs show proportional relationships between x and y.

Three of the four graphs are described by equations in the table.

Match each equation with the letter of the graph it describes.

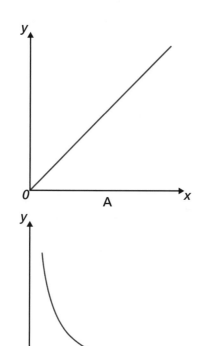

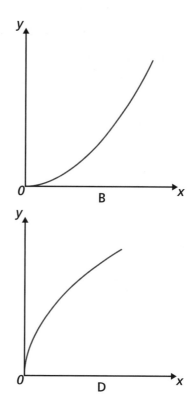

Equation	$y = \dfrac{k}{x}$	$y = kx$	$y = kx^2$
Graph			

_____

_____

_____   **3 marks**

Ratio and proportion checkpoint challenge

5. y is directly proportional to x.

When $y = 160$, $x = 8$.

a) Find a formula for y in terms of x.

_____

_____

_____ **3 marks**

b) Calculate the value of y when $x = 15$.

_____ **1 mark**

6. P is directly proportional to the square of t.

Julius says that when t is doubled, the value of P is also doubled.

Julius is wrong. Explain why.

_____ **1 mark**

7. M is inversely proportional to n^2.

$M = 75$ when $n = 4$.

Find the value of n when $M = 48$.

_____

_____

_____

_____ **4 marks**

61

Ratio and proportion checkpoint challenge

8. Philip has two cubes. The side length of cube 1 is 6 m. The volumes of cube 1 and cube 2 are in the ratio $8:27$.
   Find the surface area of cube 2.

   _____

   _____

   _____

   _____
   4 marks

9. Given that $x + 1 : x - 1 = x + 1 : 2x$, find the value of x.

   _____

   _____

   _____

   _____
   5 marks

Total marks = 30

MATHS HIGHER

Geometry and measures checkpoint challenge

 Worked example 1

The area of a plot of land is $121 \, m^2$. Work out the area in cm^2.

$1 \, m = 100 \, cm$

$1 \, m^2 = 100 \times 100$

$\qquad = 10\,000 \, cm^2$

$121 \, m^2 = 121 \times 10\,000$

$\qquad = 1\,210\,000 \, cm^2$

Worked example 2

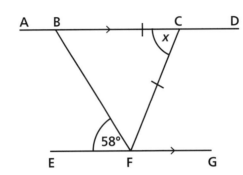

ABCD and EFG are parallel lines.

BC = CF

Angle BFE = 58°

Work out the value of the angle marked x.

Give reasons for each stage of your working.

$FBC = 58°$ because alternate angles are equal.

$BFC = 58°$ because base angles of an isosceles triangle are equal.

$x = 180 - (58 + 58)$

$\quad = 64°$ because angles in a triangle sum to 180°.

 1. A ship sails from port on a bearing of 085°.

Work out the bearing of the port from the ship.

_____

_____ **2 marks**

 2. Convert $5 \, m^3$ to cm^3.

_____

_____ **2 marks**

Edexcel

Geometry and measures checkpoint challenge

3. Triangle ABC has a perimeter of 34 cm. AB = 14 cm. BC = 9 cm.

   Is triangle ABC right-angled? Give reasons for your answer.

   _____

   _____ **3 marks**

4. The diagram shows a regular hexagon and a rectangle.

   Calculate the value of the angle marked x. 🖊

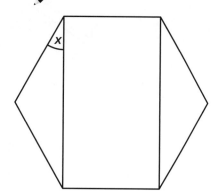

   _____

   _____

   _____ **3 marks**

5. The volume of a sphere is 288π.
   The sphere is cut exactly in half.
   Work out the total surface area of the solid hemisphere.
   Give your answer as a multiple of π.

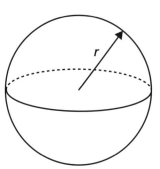

   volume of a sphere $= \dfrac{4}{3}\pi r^3$

   surface area of a sphere $= 4\pi r^2$

   _____

   _____

   _____ **3 marks**

Geometry and measures checkpoint challenge

 6. ABC and EDC are straight lines.

AE and BD are parallel.

Angle ABD = 112°

Angle BCD = 46°

Work out the value of the angle marked *x*.

Give a reason for each stage of your working.

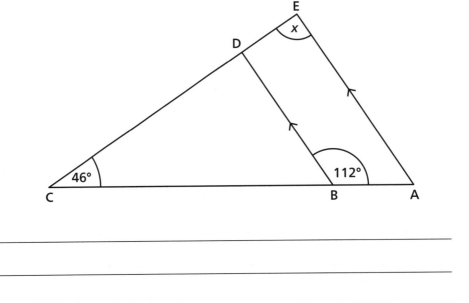

_____

_____

_____

_____

_____ **5 marks**

MATHS HIGHER

Edexcel

Geometry and measures checkpoint challenge

7. ABC and AED are straight lines.

   Angle BEA and angle CDE are both right angles.

   BE = 2 cm

   ED = 12 cm

   CD = 8 cm

   a) Work out the area of the trapezium BCDE.

   _____

   _____ **2 marks**

   b) Work out the length of AE.

   _____

   _____

   _____ **3 marks**

   c) Work out the size of the angle BAE.

   _____

   _____ **2 marks**

Geometry and measures checkpoint challenge

8. ABCDE is a solid pyramid.

ABCD is a square with sides of length 15 cm.

The angle between any sloping edge and the plane *ABCD* is 60°.

Calculate the volume of the pyramid.

Give your answer correct to the nearest whole number.

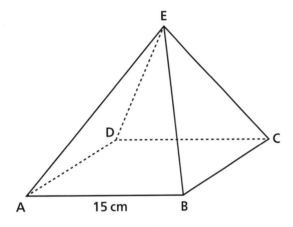

volume of a pyramid $= \frac{1}{3} \times$ area of base $\times$ vertical height

_____

_____

_____

_____

_____ **5 marks**

Total marks = 30

MATHS HIGHER

Probability checkpoint challenge

Worked example 1

A spinner can land on the number 1, 2, 3 or 4.

This table shows the probabilities of the spinner landing on each number.

Number	1	2	3	4
Probability	0.2	$x + 0.1$	$2x - 0.3$	$x + 0.2$

Work out the probability that the spinner will land on a 3.

$$0.2 + x + 0.1 + 2x - 0.3 + x + 0.2 = 1$$
$$4x + 0.2 = 1$$
$$4x = 0.8$$
$$x = 0.2$$

$$P(\text{lands on a 3}) = 2x - 0.3$$
$$= 2 \times 0.2 - 0.3$$
$$= 0.1$$

Worked example 2

A ball is thrown at a target. Given that the probability of hitting the target twice is 0.81, work out the probability of missing the target twice.

$$P(\text{hitting target}) \times P(\text{hitting target}) = 0.81$$
$$P(\text{hitting target}) = \sqrt{0.81}$$
$$= 0.9$$

$$P(\text{missing target}) = 1 - 0.9$$
$$= 0.1$$

$$P(\text{missing target twice}) = 0.1 \times 0.1$$
$$= 0.01$$

Edexcel

Probability checkpoint challenge

1. Kendrick plays a game where he can score points on a spinner labelled 1 to 5.

   The table shows information about the probability of scoring different points.

Points	1	2	3	4	5
Probability	0.12	x	$4x$	0.23	0.4

    a) Work out the value of x.

   _____

   _____

   _____ **3 marks**

   b) Kendrick plays the game twice. Work out the probability of him scoring a total of 7 points.

   _____

   _____

   _____ **3 marks**

2. Saskia designs a game with two sets of cards.

   One set of cards is numbered 1, 2, 3, 6, 8 and 9.

   The other set of cards is numbered 3, 4, 5 and 6.

   When one card is taken from each set at random, the numbers on the cards are added to get the total score.

    a) Complete the table to show all the possible total scores.

		First set					
		1	**2**	**3**	**6**	**8**	**9**
Second set	**3**	4	5				
	4	5					
	5						
	6						

   1 mark

   b) What is the probability that the total score will be 11?

   _____ **1 mark**

Probability checkpoint challenge

c) 120 people play Saskia's game once.

Each person pays 10p to play the game.

The prize for getting a total of 11 is 50p.

What is the amount of profit Saskia expects from the 120 people playing the game?

_____

_____

_____

_____

_____ **4 marks**

3. A biased dice is rolled twice. Given that the probability of it landing on six both times is 0.49, work out the probability of it not landing on six at all.

_____

_____

_____

_____ **4 marks**

4. Nasir has a biased dice.

When the dice is rolled once, the probability that it will land on 5 is $\frac{2}{3}$.

Nasir is going to roll the dice twice.

a) Complete the probability tree diagram.

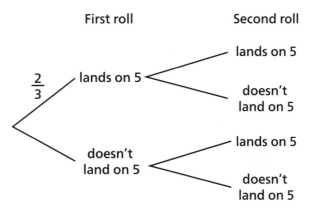

2 marks

b) Work out the probability that the dice **will not** land on a 5 on the first roll and **will** land on 5 on the second roll.

_____

_____ **2 marks**

Probability checkpoint challenge

 5. Here is a Venn diagram.

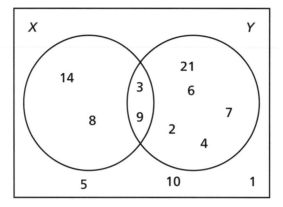

a) Write the numbers that are in set X'.

_____ **1 mark**

b) Write the numbers that are in set $X \cap Y$.

_____

_____ **1 mark**

c) One of the numbers in the diagram is chosen at random.

Find the probability that the number is in set $X \cup Y$.

_____

_____ **2 marks**

 6. There are 5 counters in a bag. There are x green counters and all the other counters are blue.

Nathaniel takes two counters from the bag at random.

Find an expression, in terms of x, for the probability that Nathaniel takes two green counters.

_____

_____

_____ **3 marks**

 7. This table shows information about the students in Suki's year at school.

	No siblings	1 sibling	2 siblings	3 siblings
Male	17	42	38	11
Female	31	39	17	8

A student is chosen at random from this group. Given that they have 1 sibling, what is the probability that they are female?

_____

_____ **3 marks**

Total marks = 30

Edexcel

Statistics checkpoint challenge

Worked example 1

The table shows the ages of people in a book club.

Age	Number of people
$20 \leqslant a < 30$	6
$30 \leqslant a < 40$	7
$40 \leqslant a < 50$	12
$50 \leqslant a < 60$	9
$60 \leqslant a < 70$	6

Work out an estimate for the mean age of the people in the club.

Age	Number of people (f)	Mid-point (x)	fx
$20 \leqslant a < 30$	6	25	150
$30 \leqslant a < 40$	7	35	245
$40 \leqslant a < 50$	12	45	540
$50 \leqslant a < 60$	9	55	495
$60 \leqslant a < 70$	6	65	390
total	40	total	1820

$$\text{mean} = \frac{\text{sum of } fx}{\text{total frequency}}$$

$$= \frac{1820}{40}$$

$$= 45.5$$

Worked example 2

The partially completed box plot shows the time it took Marcus to complete a series of puzzles.

His median time was 30 seconds and his range was 40 seconds.

Complete the box plot.

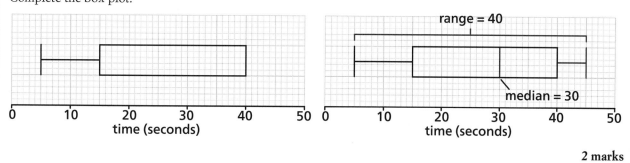

2 marks

72

Statistics checkpoint challenge

1. The table shows some information about the heights of 50 plants.

Length (a cm)	Number
$10 \leqslant a < 14$	8
$14 \leqslant a < 18$	9
$18 \leqslant a < 22$	12
$22 \leqslant a < 26$	14
$26 \leqslant a < 30$	7

a) Write the modal class interval.

_____

1 mark

b) Calculate an estimate for the mean height.

_____

_____

_____

_____

3 marks

MATHS HIGHER

Statistics checkpoint challenge

2. The scatter graph shows information about nine students' marks in an English test and in a maths test.

   The table gives the same information for two more students.

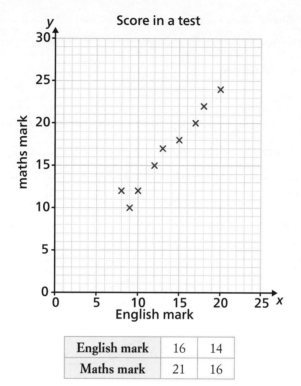

English mark	16	14
Maths mark	21	16

a) Plot the information from the table onto the scatter graph.

_____

b) Describe the correlation.

_____

c) Draw a line of best fit on the scatter graph.

_____

d) Estimate the maths mark of someone who scored 11 marks in the English test.

_____

1 mark

1 mark

1 mark

1 mark

1 mark

74

Statistics checkpoint challenge

3. 150 students are members of tennis, squash and hockey clubs.

47 students play tennis and hockey.

51 students play tennis and squash.

50 students play squash and hockey.

32 students play tennis, squash and hockey.

20 students only play tennis.

There are 8 more students that only play hockey than there are that only play squash.

Complete the Venn diagram to show this information.

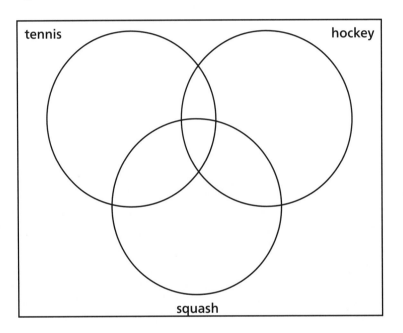

4 marks

4. The ages of four people are given as $x + 7$, $x - 6$, $x + 10$ and $x + 9$.

Their median age is 24.

Work out the age of the youngest person.

_____

_____

_____

_____ **4 marks**

MATHS HIGHER

Statistics checkpoint challenge

5. Michael did a series of spelling tests.

Here are the numbers of words he spelled correctly in each test:

12   12   13   13   14   18   18   22   24   24   24   27   27   30   30

a) Draw a box plot for this information.

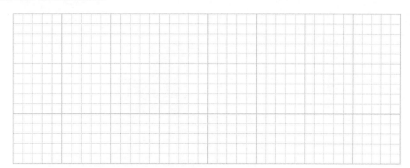

3 marks

b) Kevin did the same spelling tests.
The median number of spellings Kevin got right is 21.
His interquartile range is 12.
His range is 16.

Who is more consistent at spelling, Michael or Kevin?
Give a reason for your answer.

_____

_____

_____

_____   **2 marks**

6. This table gives information about the students at Genevieve's school.

	Male	Female	Total
KS3	128		294
KS4	156	142	
Total			

Genevieve wants to take a stratified sample of 80 students at her school to find out how many plan to go to university.

a) Complete the table.   **1 mark**

b) How many female KS4 students should Genevieve include in her survey?

_____

_____

_____   **3 marks**

Statistics checkpoint challenge

7. The histogram shows the times students took to travel to school.

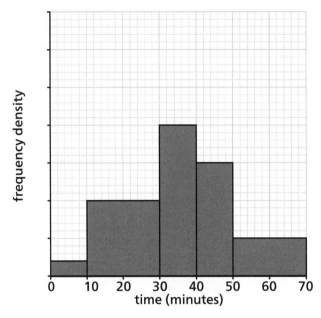

a) The number of students who take between 10 and 30 minutes to travel to school is 300.

Complete this frequency table.

Time (minutes)	Frequency
$0 < t \leq 10$	
$10 < t \leq 30$	300
$30 < t \leq 40$	
$40 < t \leq 50$	
$50 < t \leq 70$	

3 marks

b) Work out the percentage of students that took more than 35 minutes to travel to school.

_____

_____ **2 marks**

Total marks = 30

Edexcel

MATHS HIGHER

GCSE
Mathematics
Paper 1 Higher tier

1 hour 30 minutes

Materials

For this paper you must have:

- ruler
- protractor
- pair of compasses
- tracing paper.

You must **not** use a calculator.

Instructions

- Answer **all** of the questions.
- Answer all questions in the spaces provided.
- For each calculation, clearly show how you have worked out your answer.

Information

- The marks for each question are given in brackets.
- The maximum mark for the entire paper is 80.
- You may use more answer paper, graph paper and tracing paper.

MATHS HIGHER

Practice paper 1H

---

1 Mark, Sarah and Paul share £350 in the ratio $1:2:4$.

Work out how much each person gets.

Mark £ ....

Sarah £ ....

Paul £ ....

(Total for Question 1 is 3 marks)

---

2 Work out $3\frac{2}{5} - 1\frac{2}{3}$.

....

(Total for Question 2 is 3 marks)

---

3 Work out an estimate for $\sqrt{102.36 - 3.2 \times 10.8}$.

....

(Total for Question 3 is 3 marks)

Practice paper IH

4   Work out the size of the largest angle in this triangle.

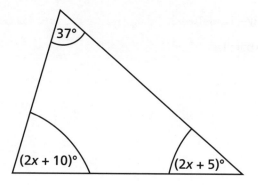

....°

(Total for Question 4 is 3 marks)

5   A landscape gardener sows grass seed on a lawn.

The lawn is in the shape of a right-angled triangle.

The grass seed costs £1.50 per m².

Work out the cost of the grass seed used for the lawn.

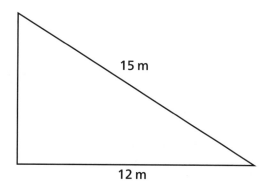

£ ....

(Total for Question 5 is 5 marks)

6 The equation of the line L_1 is $y = 4x + 5$.

The equation of the line L_2 is $3y - 12x + 10 = 0$.

Show that these two lines are parallel.

....

(Total for Question 6 is 2 marks)

7 Write 2.36×10^5 as an ordinary number.

....

(Total for Question 7 is 1 mark)

8 Work out the value of $(3.4 \times 10^5) \times (4 \times 10^{-2})$.

Give your answer in standard form.

....

(Total for Question 8 is 2 marks)

9 There are 10 boys and 20 girls in a nursery.

The mean age of all the children in the nursery is 25 months.

The mean age of the boys is 31 months.

Work out the mean age of the girls.

....

(Total for Question 9 is 3 marks)

10 A computer shop has a sale.

All its computers have been reduced by 30%.

Simon buys a computer for £420.

What was the price of the computer before the sale?

£ ....

(Total for Question 10 is 2 marks)

11 Edward played a computer game.

These are the points he scored in each game:

| 20 | 22 | 22 | 23 | 24 | 24 | 25 | 26 | 26 | 26 | 27 | 28 | 28 | 29 | 29 |

a) Draw a box plot of this information.

(3)

b) Fernando played the same computer game 15 times and recorded his scores.

The median number of points Fernando scored was 27.

The interquartile range of his scores is 3.

The range of his scores is 8.

Whose scores are more consistent, Edward's or Fernando's?

You must give a reason for your answer.

....

....

....

(2)

(Total for Question 11 is 5 marks)

Practice paper 1H

12 Show that $(x + 2)(x + 3)(x - 4)$ can be written in the form $ax^3 + bx^2 + cx + d$.

....

(Total for Question 12 is 3 marks)

13 Find the value of the following expressions.

a) $\sqrt[3]{27 \times 10^9}$

....

(2)

b) $36^{\frac{1}{2}} \times 8^{\frac{1}{3}}$

....

(2)

(Total for Question 13 is 4 marks)

14 Solve $2^{3x} = \dfrac{1}{64}$.

$x = $ ....

(Total for Question 14 is 2 marks)

15 Look at the triangle.

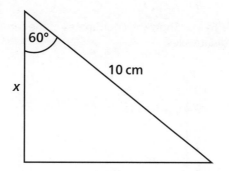

a) Write the exact value of sin 60°.

....

(1)

b) Given that cos 60° = 0.5, work out the value of x.

$x =$ ....

(2)

(Total for Question 15 is 3 marks)

16 Solve the simultaneous equations $2x + 3y = -5$ and $3x - 4y = 18$.

$x =$ ....

$y =$ ....

(Total for Question 16 is 3 marks)

17 Find the integer value of x that satisfies the inequalities $4x - 2 > 6$ and $5x - 3 < 17$.

$x =$ .... **(3)**

(Total for Question 17 is 3 marks)

18 A graph has equation $f(x) = x^2 - 6x + 2$.

a) Sketch the graph of $f(x) = x^2 - 6x + 2$. Show the coordinates of the turning point and the coordinates of any intercepts with the coordinate axes.

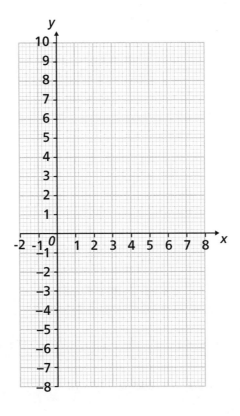

(4)

b) Hence, or otherwise, determine whether $f(x + 1) - 2 = 0$ has any real roots.
Give reasons for your answer.

....

....

(2)

(Total for Question 18 is 6 marks)

19 Make a the subject of $3ab + 6 = 4a + b$.

....

(Total for Question 19 is 3 marks)

Practice paper 1H

---

20 Simplify fully $\dfrac{(\sqrt{2}-3)(\sqrt{2}+3)}{\sqrt{5}}$.

You must show your working.

....

(Total for Question 20 is 3 marks)

---

21 The diagram shows a solid hemisphere.

The volume of the hemisphere is $\dfrac{128}{3}\pi$.

Work out the exact total surface area of the solid hemisphere.

Give your answer as a multiple of π.

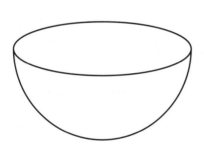

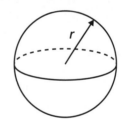

volume of sphere $= \dfrac{4}{3}\pi r^3$

surface area of sphere $= 4\pi r^2$

.... cm^2

(Total for Question 21 is 4 marks)

MATHS HIGHER

Practice paper 1H

22 Solid A and solid B are mathematically similar.

The ratio of the surface area of solid A to the surface area of solid B is 9 : 16.

The volume of solid B is 320 cm³.

Work out the volume of solid A.

.... cm³

(Total for Question 22 is 3 marks)

23 A biased dice is rolled twice.

Given that the probability of it landing a five on both rolls is 0.81, work out the probability of it not landing on a five either time.

.... **(4)**

(Total for Question 23 is 4 marks)

24 The functions f and g are such that $f(x) = 4 - 2x$ and $g(x) = 2x^2$.

a) Show that $gf(1) = 8$.

.... **(3)**

b) Work out the value of x where $f^{-1}(x) = -1$.

$x =$ .... **(4)**

(Total for Question 24 is 7 marks)

TOTAL FOR PAPER IS 80 MARKS

END OF QUESTIONS

GCSE
Mathematics
Paper 2 Higher tier

1 hour 30 minutes

Materials

For this paper you must have:

- ruler
- protractor
- pair of compasses
- tracing paper
- calculator.

Instructions

- Answer **all** of the questions.
- Answer all questions in the spaces provided.
- For each calculation, clearly show how you have worked out your answer.

Information

- The marks for each question are given in brackets.
- The maximum mark for the entire paper is 80.
- You may use more answer paper, graph paper and tracing paper.

1 Write 0.37 as a fraction.

....

(Total for Question 1 is 1 mark)

2 Find the reciprocal of 0.1.

....

(Total for Question 2 is 1 mark)

3 Find the exact value of $(3.6 - 0.65)^2 + \sqrt[3]{12.167}$.

....

(Total for Question 3 is 2 marks)

4 Here is part of a map showing the position of airport A. B is a plane 72 km from A on a bearing of 070°.

N

A ✗

a) Construct a diagram to show the position of plane B.

Use a scale of 1 cm : 24 km.

(2)

b) Write the bearing of A from B.

....

(1)

(Total for Question 4 is 3 marks)

5 James invested £8000 in a savings account.

He was paid 3% per annum compound interest.

How many years would it take James to have more than £9000 in his account?

....

(Total for Question 5 is 2 marks)

6 This diagram shows a regular hexagon and two squares.

Find the value of the angle marked *x*. You must show all your working.

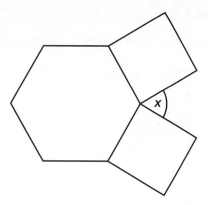

x =...°

(Total for Question 6 is 3 marks)

7 In a college, 60% of the students are boys.

a) Write the ratio of the boys to girls.

Give your answer in the form 1 : *n*.

....

(2)

b) The ratio of boys to girls at a different college is 3 : 7. What fraction of the students are boys?

....

(1)

(Total for Question 7 is 3 marks)

8 Prove algebraically that the recurring decimal $0.1\dot{4}$ can be written as the fraction $\dfrac{13}{90}$.

....

(Total for Question 8 is 2 marks)

9 This diagram shows a right-angled triangle with sides *a*, *b* and *c*.

b is 5.4 cm correct to the nearest mm.

c is 9.7 cm correct to the nearest mm.

Calculate the lower bound for *a*. Write all of the numbers on your calculator display.

You must show your working.

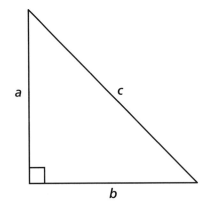

.... cm

(Total for Question 9 is 4 marks)

10 Given that $2(x - 5c) = 5 - 3x$, where *c* is an integer, show that *x* is always an odd number.

....

(Total for Question 10 is 3 marks)

11 C is a curve with equation $y = x^2 - 5x + 8$.

L is a straight line with equation $y = 2x - 2$.

L intersects C at two points, A and B.

Calculate the exact length of AB.

....

(Total for Question 11 is 6 marks)

12 Factorise these expressions.

a) $8s + 12$

....

(1)

b) $x^2 + 4x - 21$

....

(2)

(Total for Question 12 is 3 marks)

Edexcel

13 At 8 am, Sarah began a car journey.

From 8 am to 8.42 am, she drove at an average speed of 40 km/h.

From 8.42 am to 9.45 am, she drove a further 56 km.

a) Complete this distance–time graph to show Sarah's journey.

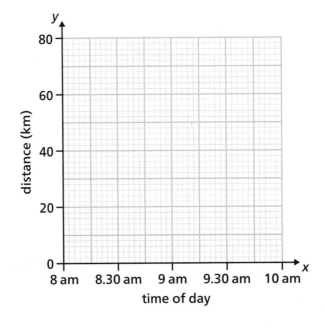

(3)

b) From 9.45 am to 10 am, Sarah travelled at an average speed of 60 km/h.

Work out the distance Sarah travelled between 9.45 am and 10 am.

.... km

(2)

(Total for Question 13 is 5 marks)

Practice paper 2H

14 A machine cuts pieces of wood.

The frequency table shows the lengths of some pieces of wood cut by the machine.

Length	Frequency
$0 \leq a < 10$	2
$10 \leq a < 20$	4
$20 \leq a < 30$	7
$30 \leq a < 40$	12
$40 \leq a < 50$	8
$50 \leq a < 60$	7

a) On the grid, plot a cumulative frequency graph for this information.

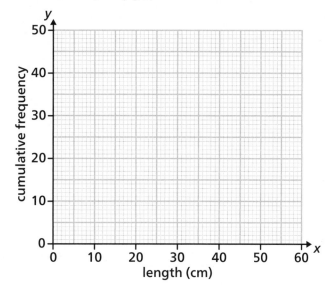

(3)

b) Find the median length of the pieces of wood.

....

(1)

c) If a piece of wood is less than 20 cm long, it is discarded.

What percentage of the pieces of wood are discarded?

....

(3)

(Total for Question 14 is 7 marks)

15 The table shows the number of emails the employees of a company received in one day.

Number of emails	Number of employees
$10 < n \le 14$	3
$14 < n \le 18$	7
$18 < n \le 22$	9
$22 < n \le 26$	
$26 < n \le 30$	4

The estimated mean number of emails received is 20.

Work out the number of employees in the $22 < n \le 26$ group.

....

(Total for Question 15 is 4 marks)

16 Here are the first five terms of a quadratic sequence.

$$4 \quad 9 \quad 16 \quad 36 \quad 49$$

Find an expression, in terms of n, for the nth term of this quadratic sequence.

....

(Total for Question 16 is 3 marks)

17 Simon asked 40 people whether they had received an email, a voicemail or a text message during the day.

All 40 people had received at least one type of message.

8 people had received an email, voicemail and a text.

2 people had only received a voicemail and an email.

3 people had only received an email and a text.

5 people had only received a voicemail and a text.

6 people had only received a voicemail.

7 people had only received an email.

Simon selects one of the 40 people at random.

a) By drawing a Venn diagram, work out the probability that this person received a text message.

....

(4)

b) Given that this person received a voicemail, find the probability that they also received an email.

....

(2)

(Total for Question 18 is 6 marks)

MATHS HIGHER

Practice paper 2H

18 On the grid, enlarge the triangle ABC by scale factor −2 using the centre (0, 1).

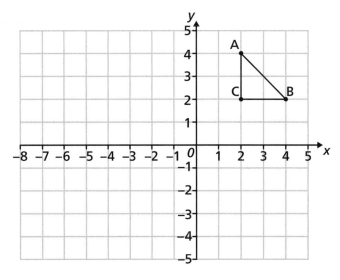

(Total for Question 17 is 2 marks)

19 ABC is a triangle.

D is a point on AB.

Work out the area of triangle BCD.

Give your answer correct to 3 significant figures.

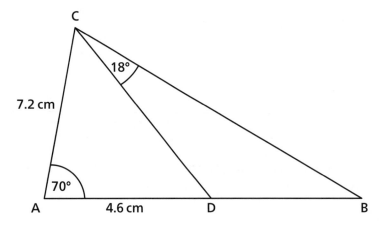

.... cm²

(Total for Question 19 is 5 marks)

20 Mark takes part in a cycling race.

The graph shows his speed in metres per second, *t* seconds after the start of the race.

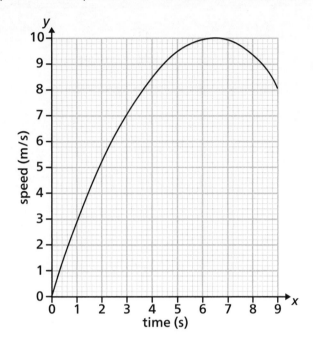

a) Calculate an estimate for the gradient of the graph when *t* = 3.

You must show how you get your answer.

....

(3)

b) Describe fully what your answer to part a) represents.

....

....

(2)

c) Explain why your answer to part a) is only an estimate.

....

....

(1)

(Total for Question 20 is 6 marks)

Practice paper 2H

21 Here is a sketch of part of the graph of $y = pq^x$, where $q > 0$.

The points $(0, 3)$, $(3, k)$ and $(5, 96)$ are all on the graph of $y = pq^x$.

Find the value of k.

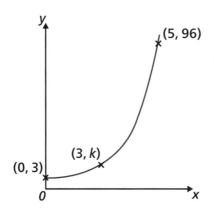

.... **(4)**

(Total for Question 21 is 4 marks)

22 An equation is defined as $x^3 + 3x = 9$.

a) Show that the equation has a solution between 1 and 2.

(2)

b) $x^3 + 3x = 8$ can be rearranged to give $x = \sqrt[3]{9 - 3x}$.

Starting with $x_0 = 1$, use the iteration formula $x_{n+1} = \sqrt[3]{9 - 3x_n}$ to find x_1 and x_2.

....

(2)

c) Find the solution to equation $x^3 + 3x = 8$. Give your answer to 3 decimal places.

....

(1)

(Total for Question 22 is 5 marks)

TOTAL FOR PAPER IS 80 MARKS

Edexcel

MATHS HIGHER

GCSE
Mathematics
Paper 3 Higher tier

1 hour 30 minutes

Materials

For this paper you must have:

- ruler
- protractor
- pair of compasses
- tracing paper
- calculator.

Instructions

- Answer **all** of the questions.
- Answer all questions in the spaces provided.
- For each calculation, clearly show how you have worked out your answer.

Information

- The marks for each question are given in brackets.
- The maximum mark for the entire paper is 80.
- You may use more answer paper, graph paper and tracing paper.

100

TUTORS GUILD **MATHS** HIGHER

Practice paper 3H

1 The sets *E*, *A* and *B* are defined as:

- *E* = {even positive numbers less than 30}

- *A* = {4, 8, 12, 16, 20, 24, 28}

- *B* = {6, 12, 18, 24}.

a) Complete the Venn diagram to represent this information.

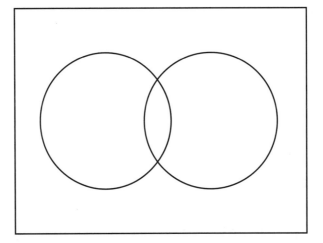

(4)

b) A number is chosen at random from the universal set, *E*.

What is the probability that the number is in the set *A* ∩ *B*?

....

(2)

(Total for Question 1 is 6 marks)

2 A and B are two points on a line.

A has coordinates (3, 5).

B has coordinates (6, *s*).

The gradient of the line AB is 6.

Work out the value of *s*.

s = ...

(3)

(Total for Question 2 is 3 marks)

3 A biased spinner can land on the numbers 1, 2, 3 or 4.

The table shows the probability of the spinner landing on each number.

Number	1	2	3	4
Probability	$2x$	$4x - 0.3$	$x + 0.1$	$3x - 0.2$

a) Work out the probability that the spinner will land on a 2.

....

(3)

b) The spinner is used 500 times. How many times would you expect it to land on a 3?

....

(2)

(Total for Question 3 is 5 marks)

4 Angharad travels from Manchester to Leeds at an average speed of 40 mph.

She then travels from Leeds to Nottingham at an average speed of 50 mph.

Angharad takes a total time of 1 hour and 15 minutes to travel from Manchester to Leeds.

The distance from Leeds to Nottingham is 100 miles.

Work out Angharad average speed from Manchester to Nottingham. Give your answer to 2 significant figures.

.... mph

(Total for Question 4 is 5 marks)

Practice paper 3H

5 The diagram shows a sector of a circle with a radius of 5 cm.

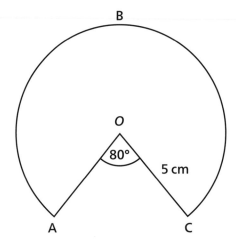

Work out the length of the arc ABC.

Give your answer correct to 3 significant figures.

.... cm

(Total for Question 5 is 2 marks)

6 **a** and **b** are vectors where $\mathbf{a} = \begin{pmatrix} 2 \\ -3 \end{pmatrix}$ and $\mathbf{b} = \begin{pmatrix} 4 \\ 2 \end{pmatrix}$.

Write the following expressions as column vectors.

a) **a** + **b**

....

(1)

b) 2**a** – 3**b**

....

(2)

(Total for Question 6 is 3 marks)

7 Shape A is reflected in the line $y = x$. The result is shape B.

Shape B is rotated 90° clockwise about (0, 0). The result is shape C.

Describe the single transformation that maps shape A onto shape C.

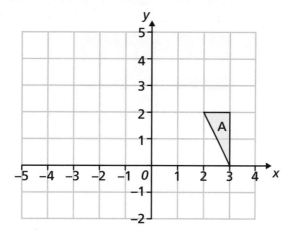

....

....

(Total for Question 7 is 3 marks)

8 ABC and AED are straight lines.

EB is parallel to DC.

AD = 10.2 cm

AE = 3.4 cm

BE = 2.7 cm

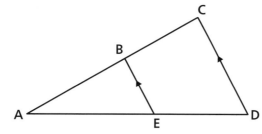

a) Work out the length of CD.

.... cm

(3)

b) AC = 7.8 cm.

Work out the length of AB.

.... cm

(2)

(Total for Question 8 is 5 marks)

9 The combination on a lock is made up of four digits. Each digit is in the range 1–9.

The first number of the combination has to be an even number from 1–9.

The rest of the numbers can be any number from 1–9.

No number can be used more than once.

Claire has forgotten her code. What is the probability she chooses the correct code on her 1st attempt?

Give your answer as a fraction.

....

(Total for Question 9 is 2 marks)

10 ABC is a right-angled triangle.

Calculate the length of AB.

Give your answer correct to 3 significant figures.

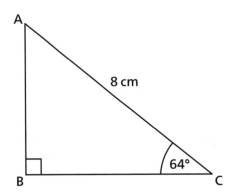

.... cm

(Total for Question 10 is 2 marks)

Practice paper 3H

11 Joseph wants to invest £5000 in a bank for 4 years.

Bank A	Bank B
compound interest	compound interest
2.5% for each year	3.8% first year
	1.3% for each extra year

Which bank will give Joseph the most interest at the end of 4 years?

You must show all your working.

....

(Total for Question 11 is 3 marks)

12 In a bag there are 5 red counters and 7 yellow counters.

Without looking, Joe picks a counter and then picks another counter without replacing the first.

a) Complete the tree diagram.

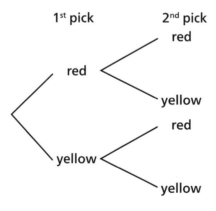

1st pick   2nd pick

red

red

yellow

yellow

red

yellow

(2)

b) Work out the probability Joe chooses two counters that are the same colour.

....

(2)

(Total for Question 12 is 4 marks)

13 A number, n, is rounded to 2 decimal places.

The result is 2.19.

Using inequalities, write the error interval for n.

....

(Total for Question 13 is 3 marks)

14 Solve $\dfrac{4x - 1}{3} + \dfrac{3x + 2}{2} = \dfrac{5x + 9}{3}$.

....

(Total for Question 14 is 4 marks)

15 Write the inequalities that define the shaded region of the graph.

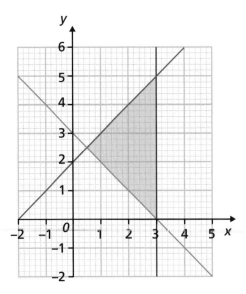

....

....

....

(Total for Question 15 is 4 marks)

Practice paper 3H

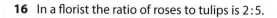

16 In a florist the ratio of roses to tulips is $2:5$.

The ratio of tulips to carnations is $8:10$.

Write the ratio of roses : carnations in its simplest form.

....

(Total for Question 16 is 3 marks)

17 Simplify $\dfrac{x^2 - 9}{2x^2 - 5x - 3}$.

....

(Total for Question 17 is 3 marks)

18 Make s the subject of the formula $t = \dfrac{3(2u-s)}{s}$.

....

(Total for Question 18 is 3 marks)

MATHS HIGHER

Practice paper 3H

19 The area of this triangle is $2\sqrt{3}\,\text{cm}^2$.

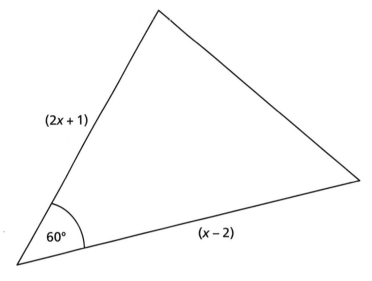

Calculate the value of x.

Give your answer correct to 3 significant figures.

....

(Total for Question 19 is 5 marks)

20 The diagram shows part of the graph of $y = x^2 - 3x + 4$.

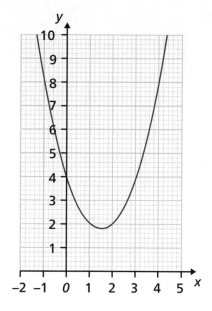

a) By drawing a suitable straight line, use the graph to find estimates for the solutions of $x^2 - 4x + 3 = 0$.

....

(2)

b) P is the point on the graph $y = x^2 - 3x + 4$ where $x = 3$.

Calculate an estimate for the gradient of the graph at the point P.

....

(3)

(Total for Question 20 is 5 marks)

21 The point (4, 2) lies on a circle with its centre at (0, 0).

Work out the equation of the circle.

....

(Total for Question 21 is 2 marks)

22 The histogram shows the percentage mark some students achieved on a maths test.

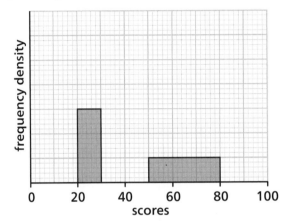

a) Complete the frequency table and the histogram.

Percentage	Frequency
$0 < t \le 20$	12
$20 < t \le 30$	12
$30 < t \le 50$	16
$50 < t \le 80$	
$80 < t \le 100$	24

(3)

b) Work out the percentage of students that scored more than 70 marks.

....

(2)

(Total for Question 22 is 5 marks)

TOTAL FOR PAPER IS 80 MARKS

END OF QUESTIONS

Topic test answers

1 Diagnostic lesson

1. $x = 1$, $y = 4$ or $x = 4$, $y = 2$
2. $a = 2$ (*2 marks: 1 mark for method, 1 mark for correct answer*)
3. Marcus did not carry the 1 correctly in the first row from $(3 \times 3) + 1 = 10$.
He also did not write a 0 in the units column of the second row when multiplying by 20.
The correct working would be:

```
          2   3   4
    ×         2   3
        ─────────────
          7   0   2
          1   1
    +   4   6   8   0
        ─────────────
        5   3   8   2
        1
```

(3 marks: 1 mark for each mistake found and 1 mark for correct multiplication)
4. a) 206.64   b) 2066.4   c) 24.6
5. Answers include shape B as the others are prisms, or shape A because it has no vertices.

2 Number: Standard form

1. a) 2.3×10^4 b) 4.5×10^{-5}
2. 10^{-3}, 3×10^{-2}, 3^0, 0.1×10^2 (*1 mark for two or three numbers in correct order, 2 marks for all four in correct order*)
3. 2×10^3
4. 2.4×10^7 (*2 marks: 1 mark for evidence of a correct method, 1 mark for correct answer*)
5. 4.23×10^{-3} (*2 marks: 1 mark for evidence of a correct method, 1 mark for correct answer*)
6. 317 (*2 marks: 1 mark for evidence of a correct method, 1 mark for correct answer*)

3 Number: Surds

1. a) $4\sqrt{7}$ b) $5\sqrt{3}$ c) $6\sqrt{5}$ d) 2
2. $5^{\frac{-1}{3}}$
3. $3 + \sqrt{3}$ (*2 marks: 1 mark for expansion, 1 mark for full simplification*)
4. $2\sqrt{3}$
5.
$$\frac{(1 + \sqrt{2})}{(3 - \sqrt{2})} = \frac{(1 + \sqrt{2})(3 + \sqrt{2})}{(3 - \sqrt{2})(3 + \sqrt{2})}$$
$$= \frac{3 + \sqrt{2} + 3\sqrt{2} + 2}{9 + 3\sqrt{2} - 3\sqrt{2} - 2}$$
$$= \frac{5 + 4\sqrt{2}}{7}$$
$$= \frac{1}{7}(5 + 4\sqrt{2})$$

(2 marks: 1 mark for method of rationalising denominator, 1 mark for correct simplification)

4 Number: Roots and indices

1. $(-1)^4 = 5^0$

$\sqrt[3]{27} = 9^{\frac{1}{2}}$

$64^{\frac{1}{2}} = 2^3$

(1 mark for two correct answers, 2 marks for all three correct)
2. 5
3. 100 (*2 marks: 1 mark for a correct method, 1 mark for correct answer*)

4. a) 9   b) $\frac{25}{9}$ (*2 marks: 1 mark for method, 1 mark for correct answer*)

5. 2^4 (*2 marks: 1 mark for method, 1 mark for correct answer*)

Topic test answers

5 Number: Factors and multiples

1. $2 \times 3 \times 3 \times 7$

2. $2 \times 3 \times 5 \times 5 \times 7$ (or $2 \times 3 \times 5^2 \times 7$) *(2 marks: 2 marks for at least 4 correct divisions, 1 mark for 2 correct divisions)*

3. 42 *(2 marks: 1 mark for writing at least one number in terms of prime factors or identifying a common factor other than 1, 1 mark for correct answer)*

4. 5 packs of crisps, 6 packs of drink, 10 packs of chocolate bars *(2 marks: 1 mark for finding common multiples and starting to find number of packs, 1 mark for correct answer)*

5. a) $2^3 \times 3^2 \times 5$ b) $2^6 \times 3^2 \times 5^2$ *(2 marks: 1 mark for $14\,400 = 120^2$ and $120^2 = (2^3 \times 3 \times 5)^2$, 1 mark for correct answer)*

6 Number: Calculations

1. a) $4\dfrac{7}{15}$ b) $4\dfrac{7}{8}$

2. 3 *(2 marks: 1 mark for $\dfrac{5}{3} \div \dfrac{3}{4}$ or $\dfrac{5}{3} \times \dfrac{4}{3}$, 1 mark for correct answer)*

3. $\dfrac{\pi}{20}$

4. a) 10   b) 20   c) 17

5. a) $2^2 \times 3 \times 7$ b) $2^5 \times 3^2 \times 7$

7 Number: Percentages and fractions

1. $\dfrac{1}{200}$

2. 120×1.025

3. £320 *(2 marks: 1 mark for process to find original price, 1 mark for correct answer)*

4. £158.02 *(2 marks: 1 mark for process to find price after four years, 1 mark for correct answer)*

5. $1.14 \times 0.92 = 1.0488$, which is approximately equivalent to a 5% increase *(2 marks: 1 mark for process to find percentage increase, 1 mark for correct answer)*

6. £30 000 *(2 marks: 1 mark for method, 1 mark for correct answer)*

8 Number: Rounding and estimation

1. $4.75\,\text{m} < \text{length} \leqslant 4.85\,\text{m}$ *(2 marks: 1 mark for 4.75 m and 4.85 m, 1 mark for the correct order)*

2. $\dfrac{13}{90}$ *(2 marks: 1 mark for a correct method, 1 mark for correct answer)*

3. $2.335^2\,cm^2 < \text{area} \leqslant 2.345^2\,cm^2$ or $5.452\,225\,cm^2 < \text{area} \leqslant 5.499\,025\,cm^2$ *(3 marks: 1 mark for 2.335 and 2.345 seen, 1 mark for 2.335^2 and $2.345^2\,cm^2$ or 5.452 225 and 5.499 025, 1 mark for correct order)*

4. 124 seconds, 122 seconds *(3 marks: 1 mark for finding bounds, 1 mark for calculating upper bound and lower bound time, 1 mark for correct answer)*

9 Algebra: Introducing algebra

1. a) $x = \pm 7$ b) $x = \sqrt{y + 5}$

2. $2x^2 - x - 6$

3. $(x + 1)(x - 2)(x + 4) = (x^2 + x - 2x - 2)(x + 4)$
$$= x^3 + x^2 - 2x^2 - 2x + 4x^2 + 4x - 8x - 8$$
$$= x^3 + 3x^2 - 6x - 8$$
(2 marks: 1 mark for full expansion, 1 mark for full simplification)

4. a) $f(2) = 7$ b) $fg(x) = 3x^2 + 1$ c) $gf(x) = (3x + 1)^2$
$$= 9x^2 + 6x + 1$$

d) $f^{-1}(x) = \dfrac{x - 1}{3}$ *(2 marks: 1 mark for method to find inverse function, 1 mark for correct answer)*

Edexcel

MATHS HIGHER

Topic test answers

10 Algebra: Solving linear equations

1. Chris is 21 years old.

2. a) $x = -6$ b) $x = -6.67$ c) $x = \pm6$ d) $x = 1$

3. $x = 15$ *(2 marks: 1 mark for $2x + 50 = 4x + 20$, 1 mark for correct answer)*

4. $x = 7$ so perimeter $= 50\,\text{cm}$ *(3 marks: 1 mark for setting up an equation to find x, 1 mark for $x = 7$, 1 mark for correct answer)*

11 Algebra: Solving quadratic equations

1. a) $x = -3$, $x = 4$ b) $x = -\dfrac{1}{2}$, $x = \dfrac{5}{3}$

2. a) $x = -2$, $x = 6$ *(2 marks: 1 mark for factorisation, 1 mark for correct answer)*

     b) $x = -\dfrac{3}{2}$, $x = 1$ *(2 marks: 1 mark for factorisation, 1 mark for correct answer)*

3. $x = -1 - 2\sqrt{2}$, $x = 2\sqrt{2} - 1$ *(2 marks: 1 mark for completing the square, 1 mark for correct answers)*

4. $x = \dfrac{1}{3}$, $x = -2$ *(2 marks: 1 mark for substitution into quadratic formula, 1 mark for correct answers)*

12 Algebra: Simultaneous equations

1. a) $x = 2$, $y = 4$ *(2 marks: 1 mark for each variable)*

     b) $a = 5$, $b = \dfrac{1}{2}$ *(2 marks: 1 mark for each variable)*

2. adult ticket $= £25$, child ticket $= £15.50$ *(3 marks: 1 mark for setting up a pair of simultaneous equations, 1 mark for price of an adult ticket, 1 mark for price of a child ticket)*

3. graph shown right

     $x = -1$, $y = 2$ and $x = 2$, $y = 5$ *(3 marks: 1 mark for correct graph of $y = x^2 + 1$, 1 mark for $y = x + 3$, 1 mark for values of x and y)*

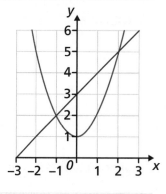

13 Algebra: Iteration

1. $x_1 = 4.408\,163\ldots$, $x_2 = 4.257\,308\ldots$, $x_3 = 4.275\,866\ldots$ *(3 marks: 1 mark for each iteration)*

2. a) $x^3 + 3x = 7$ so $x^3 + 3x - 7 = f(x)$

     $f(1) = -3$

     $f(2) = 7$

     $f(1)$ is negative and $f(2)$ is positive, so there is a root between $x = 1$ and $x = 2$. *(2 marks: 1 mark for method to find at least 1 root, 1 mark for correct explanation)*

     b) $x(x^2 + 3) = 7$ so $x = \dfrac{7}{x^2 + 3}$ *(2 marks: 1 mark for at least 1 correct step and no incorrect steps, 1 mark for correct answer)*

     c) 1.41 *(3 marks: 1 mark for correct substitution into iterative formula, 1 mark for re-substituting until 1.41 appears twice in a row, 1 mark for correct answer)*

14 Algebra: Inequalities

1. $-2, -1, 0, 1$

2. $-4 < x \leqslant 3$

3. $a \geqslant -5$

4. $-2, -1, 0, 1, 2$ *(2 marks: 1 mark for method, 1 mark for correct answer)*

5. $-3, -2, -1, 0, 1, 2, 3$

6. $x \leqslant 6$ *(2 marks: 1 mark for method, 1 mark for correct answer)*

7. $-2 < x < 3$ *(2 marks: 1 mark for method, 1 mark for correct answer)*

MATHS HIGHER

Topic test answers

15 Algebra: Sequences

1. A: geometric; B: quadratic; C: arithmetic *(2 marks: 1 mark for one correct, 2 marks for all three correct)*

2. A: $2 \times 2^{n+1}$; B: $n^2 + 2n$; C: $4n + 3$ *(6 marks: 1 mark for method to deduce n^{th} term for each sequence, 1 mark for each correct answer)*

3. 5 *(2 marks: 1 mark for method leading to $n = 5.477$, 1 mark for correct answer)*

16 Algebra: Linear, quadratic, cubic and reciprocal graphs

1. a) A and C   b) B and D

2. $y = 4x + 3$ *(2 marks: 1 mark for finding the gradient, 1 mark for finding c)*

3. $y = -\frac{1}{2}x + 10$ *(2 marks: 1 mark for finding the gradient, 1 mark for finding c)*

4. a)

x	−8	−7	−6	−5	−4	−3	−2	−1	0
y	12	5	0	−3	−4	−3	0	5	12

b) graph shown right

c) (−6, 0) (−2, 0)

d) (−4, −4)

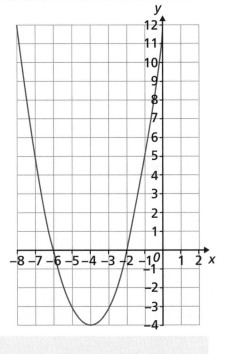

17 Algebra: Interpreting graphs

1. a) 100 km   b) 30 minutes   c) 40 km/h

d) Between 100 and 140 minutes, because the gradient of the line is the steepest.   e) 75 km/h

2. a) answers around $35 \, \text{m/s}^2$ (will depend on the student's tangent) *(2 marks: 1 mark for constructing tangent on graph, 1 mark for calculating acceleration based on tangent)*

b) $t = 3$ seconds as the gradient of the tangent at this point is zero.

c) answers around 40 m (will depend on how the student works out the area) *(2 marks: 1 mark for a method to work out area, 1 mark for answer based on method)*

18 Algebra: Trigonometric graphs and transformations

1. A = tan x B = sin x C = cos x *(1 mark for one correct, 2 marks for all three correct)*

2. Yes – the sin x graph is shifted 90° to the left which is the same as the cos x graph.

3. a) shown bottom left

b) shown bottom middle

c) shown bottom right

4. a) reflection in the x-axis

b) move left 4 units

5. (3, 2) *(2 marks: 1 mark for each coordinate)*

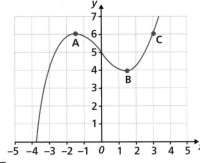 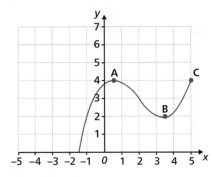 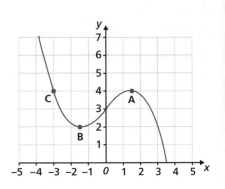

Topic test answers

19 Algebra: Graphs of circles

1. a) $(0, 0)$ b) 5   c) $(3, 4)$

2. a) $x^2 + y^2 = 9$ b) $x^2 + y^2 = 36$

3.

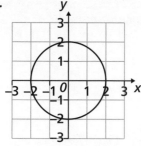

(2 marks: 1 mark for correct centre, 1 mark for correct radius)

4. a) $\dfrac{1}{3}$ b) $y = -3x + 10$ *(2 marks: 1 mark for correct gradient, 1 mark for correct value of c)*

20 Ratio, proportion and rates of change: Ratio

1. 75° *(2 marks: 1 mark for process to find largest angle e.g. $\dfrac{180}{12} \times 5$, 1 mark for correct answer)*

2. 1:3 *(2 marks: 1 mark for $\dfrac{1}{3}$:1, 1 mark for correct answer)*

3. $1 : 2\dfrac{1}{3}$

4. 192 *(2 marks: 1 mark for a process to find the number of men and the number of women, 1 mark for correct answer)*

5. $t = \dfrac{3}{2}l$

6. £176 *(2 marks: 1 mark for process to find 1 share, 1 mark for correct answer)*

21 Ratio, proportion and rates of change: Bearings and scale

1. a) 12 km   b) 5 cm

2. Circle; radius

3. a) 210°, 8 km *(2 marks: 1 mark for bearing, 1 mark for distance)*
     b) C marked on a bearing of 120° from A and 2.5 cm from A.

4.

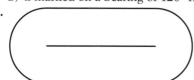

(2 marks: 1 mark for all points a constant distance from the line, 1 mark for all points 1 cm from the line)

5. 280° *(2 marks: 1 mark for process to find bearing, 1 mark for correct answer)*

22 Ratio, proportion and rates of change: Direct and inverse proportion

1. a) graph shown right
     b) It does not show direct proportion as the graph does not go through the origin.

2. a) 60 minutes   b) 10 minutes

3. a) € 452   b) £ 176.99
     c) It is cheaper in Spain.
     d) $P = 1.13 \times E$

4. a) $S = \dfrac{40}{T}$ b) $S = 10$

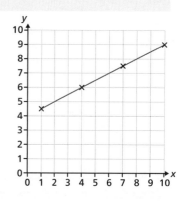

Topic test answers

23 Ratio, proportion and rates of change: Rates of change

1. $400 \times 1.15^4 = 700$ *(2 marks: 1 mark for 400×1.15^4 or equivalent process to find answer, 1 mark for correct answer)*
2. a) $v = 80\,000 \times 0.92t$ b) £52 726.52
   c) 12 years *(2 marks: 1 mark for process to find number of years, 1 mark for correct answer)*
3. a) 7%   b) $p_1 = £128\,400$; $p_2 = £137\,388$; $p_3 = £147\,005.16$ *(3 marks: 1 mark for each answer)*

24 Geometry and measures: Angles

1. 250° *(2 marks; 1 mark for method, 1 mark for answer)*
2. a) 24 sides   b) 8 sides
3. 150°
4. 12 sides *(2 marks; 1 marks for finding x, 1 mark for correct answer)*
5. 120° *(3 marks; 1 mark for finding interior angle of the hexagon; 1 mark for angles at a point = 360°, 1 mark for correct angle)*

25 Geometry and measures: 2-D shapes

1. Rectangle: Opposite sides are parallel and equal in length. All angles are right angles.
   Parallelogram: Opposite sides are parallel and equal in length. Diagonals bisect one another. Opposite angles are equal.
   Kite: Two pairs of adjacent sides are equal. The shorter diagonal is bisected by the longer diagonal at right angles. One pair of opposite angles are equal.
   Rhombus: A parallelogram with all sides equal in length.
   Trapezium: Only two sides are parallel. *(4 marks: 1 mark for one correct, 2 marks for two correct, 3 marks for three correct, 4 marks for all correct)*

2.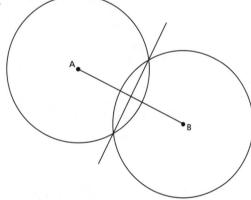

3.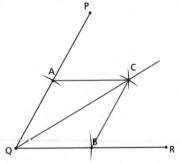

   (2 marks: 1 mark for process to bisect angle, 1 mark for correctly bisected angle)

4.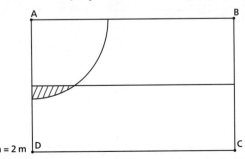

   (3 marks: 1 mark for circle 3 cm from A, 1 mark for horizontal line through the centre, 1 mark for correctly shaded area.)

Topic test answers

26 Geometry and measures: Perimeter, area and volume

1. 78 cm²
2. 5 cm
3. 20.6 cm
4. 240 cm²
5. 283 m³
6. 113 cm³ *(2 marks: 1 mark for method, 1 mark for correct answer)*

27 Geometry and measures: Pythagoras' theorem

1. 10 cm, 24 cm, 26 cm and 12 cm, 16 cm, 20 cm
2. 7.07 cm *(2 marks: 1 mark for use of Pythagoras' theorem, 1 mark for correct answer)*
3. 6.71 *(2 marks: 1 mark for use of Pythagoras' theorem, 1 mark for correct answer)*
4. 19.6 cm *(2 marks: 1 mark for use of Pythagoras' theorem, 1 mark for correct answer)*
5. 10.5 cm *(3 marks: 1 mark for use of Pythagoras' theorem, 1 mark for process to find $\sqrt{85}$, 1 mark for correct answer)*

28 Geometry and measures: Using trigonometry

1. 41.4°
2. 20.8 cm² *(2 marks: 1 mark for finding the perpendicular height of the triangle, 1 mark for correct answer)*
3. 36.5° *(2 marks: 1 mark for finding the length of the dashed line, 1 mark for correct answer)*
4. 10 km *(2 marks: 1 mark for a correct diagram showing 150 – 90 = 60, 1 mark for correct answer)*
5. a) $AC = \sqrt{8^2 + 6^2} = 10$

   $GAC = \tan^{-1}\left(\dfrac{10}{10}\right) = 45°$

   (2 marks: 1 mark for use of Pythagoras' theorem to calculate missing length, 1 mark for correct answer)
   b) 14.1 cm

29 Geometry and measures: Trigonometric values

1. $\cos 30 = \dfrac{\sqrt{3}}{2}$; $\sin 90 = 1$; $\tan 30 = \dfrac{\sqrt{3}}{3}$; $\cos 90 = 0$ *(3 marks: 1 mark for 1 correct, 2 marks for 2 correct, 3 marks for all correct)*
2. 14.9 cm *(2 marks: 1 mark for process to find length, 1 mark for correct answer)*
3. 41.5° *(2 marks: 1 mark for process to find angle, 1 mark for correct answer)*
4. 7.64 cm *(2 marks: 1 mark for process to find length, 1 mark for correct answer)*
5. 57.9 cm²

30 Geometry and measures: Circles

1. 49.5 cm²
2. 72°
3. 4.6 cm *(3 marks: 1 mark for process to find radius, 1 mark for process to find circumference of whole circle, 1 mark for correct answer)*
4. Angles on a straight line add to 180 so angle at origin = 180 – 120 = 60.
   Angles in a triangle add to 180. The two radii are equal length so the triangle is isosceles. Base angles in isosceles triangles are equal. (180 – 60) ÷ 2 = 60, so x = 60. *(3 marks: 1 mark for angles on a straight line, 1 mark for recognising that the triangle is isosceles, 1 mark for correct answer)*
5. x = 180 – 36 = 144 (opposite angles in cyclic quadrilaterals sum to 180)
   (180 – 144) ÷ 2 = y, so y = 18 (base angles in an isosceles triangle are equal, angles in a triangle sum to 180)
   (3 marks: 1 mark for correct values of x and y, 1 mark for each correct reason)

Topic test answers

31 Geometry and measures: Vectors

1. a) as shown right *(2 marks; 1 mark for each point drawn correctly)*

b) $\begin{pmatrix} 4 \\ -3 \end{pmatrix}$

c) as shown right

d) 5

2. a) $\begin{pmatrix} 6 \\ 5 \end{pmatrix}$ b) $\begin{pmatrix} 7 \\ 0 \end{pmatrix}$

3. $\overrightarrow{CA} = \mathbf{a}$ $\overrightarrow{CB} = \mathbf{b}$

$\overrightarrow{AB} = -\mathbf{a} + \mathbf{b}$

$\qquad = -(\mathbf{a} - \mathbf{b})$

$\overrightarrow{CX} = \frac{1}{2}\mathbf{a}$ $\overrightarrow{CY} = \frac{1}{2}\mathbf{b}$

$\overrightarrow{XY} = -\frac{1}{2}\mathbf{a} + \frac{1}{2}\mathbf{b}$

$\qquad = -\frac{1}{2}(\mathbf{a} - \mathbf{b})$

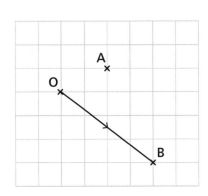

$\overrightarrow{XY}$ is a multiple of $\overrightarrow{AB}$ so the lines are parallel.

(3 marks; 1 mark for calculating $\overrightarrow{AB}$, 1 mark for calculating $\overrightarrow{XY}$, 1 mark for recognising that they are multiples and so are parallel)

32 Probability: Basic probability and Venn diagrams

1. 10

2. a) 0.06 *(2 marks: 1 mark for process to find x, 1 mark for correct answer)*   b) 88

3. a) 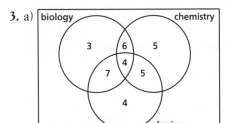   b) $\frac{4}{34} = \frac{2}{17}$

(3 marks: 1 mark for central region correct, 2 marks for four regions correct, 3 marks for all regions correct)

4. a) 6, 9, 1, 4, 8, 10   b) $\frac{1}{10}$

33 Probability: Combined probability

1. a) $\frac{1}{25}$ b) $\frac{2}{5}$ *(2 marks: 1 mark for working (i.e. listing all options), 1 mark for answer)*

2. a) *(2 marks: 1 mark for top branches correct, 1 mark for bottom branches correct)*

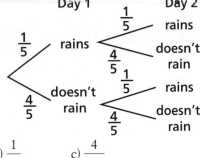

b) $\frac{1}{25}$ c) $\frac{4}{125}$

3. 0.16 *(2 marks: 1 mark for method, 1 mark for correct answer)*

4. Bal has assumed that the events are independent.

Topic test answers

34 Probability: Conditional probability

1. a) 720   b) $\frac{1}{8}$

2. a)

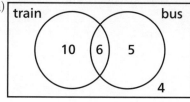

(3 marks: 1 mark for 4 being outside of circles within box, 1 mark for correct number in centre, 1 mark for correct numbers for train only and bus only)

b) $\frac{3}{8}$

3. a) $\frac{8}{43}$ *(2 marks: 1 mark for correctly finding total number of students, 1 mark for reading correct number with brown hair and green eyes)*

b) $\frac{4}{7}$ *(2 marks: 1 mark for recognising that there are 7 possible students and setting this as the denominator, 1 mark for recognising that 4 of those have green eyes)*

35 Statistics: Planning an investigation and data collection

1. a) Answers could include: The groups overlap. They have unequal width. There is no category for over 500 people. *(2 marks: 1 mark for each correct answer)*

b)

Number of people	0–99	100–199	200–299	300–399	400–499	500+
Tally						

2. B: primary, continuous

3. a) Take a sample of approximately 60 students – accept any method of randomly selecting students, such as allocating each member of the school a number and randomly generating numbers. *(2 marks: 1 mark for appropriate sample size, 1 mark for method of random selection)*

b) Split the school into year and/or gender groups and calculate the proportion in each group. Take a random sample of this proportion of 60 students. *(2 marks: 1 mark for explaining how to divide the school into categories, 1 mark for method of random selection)*

4. 140 *(2 marks: 1 mark for method, 1 mark for correct answer)*

36 Statistics: Constructing graphs, charts and diagrams

1. a)

```
      Class A                   Class B
                     2 | 7  8
       5  3  3   2 | 3 | 1  4  5  7
    7  6  5   4   2 | 4 | 2  2  4  6
    7  7  3   1   0 | 5 | 0  0  0  4  9
       9  3   2   1 | 6 | 2  3  5  7
          5   2   2 | 7 | 1  2
              1   0 | 8 | 1  3
```

b)

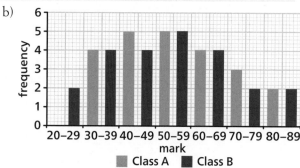

(3 marks: 1 mark for correctly filled out table, 1 mark for axes and a key, 1 mark for correctly plotted bars)

c) Advantage: the data for class A and B can be directly compared.

Disadvantage: it loses some of the accuracy from the stem-and-leaf diagram.

2. a) False; you cannot tell as you don't know how many people are included in the pie chart. *(2 marks: 1 mark for false, 1 mark for correct reason)*

b) True; 23% watched animation on Sunday. *(2 marks: 1 mark for true, 1 mark for correct reason)*

Topic test answers

37 Statistics: Interpreting data

1. a) $30 \leqslant a < 40$

b) $40 \leqslant a < 50$

c) 41.5 *(3 marks: 1 mark for using x × f to find mid-points, 1 mark for "x × f" ÷ 31, 1 mark for correct answer; accept 41 if working is seen)*

2. a)

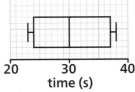

Median = 30, lower quartile = 24, upper quartile = 37 *(3 marks: 1 mark for one of the median,* lower quartile *or* upper quartile *correct, 2 marks for a fully correct box plot, only award 1 mark for a box plot with 3 of median,* lower quartile, upper quartile, *minimum or maximum correct)*

b) after three months (with reason) *(2 marks: 1 mark for calculation of interquartile range, 1 mark for correct answer and reason)*

38 Statistics: Scatter graphs, cumulative frequency graphs and histograms

1. a)

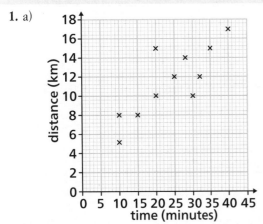

b) positive

c) 23–24 minutes

2. a) 44–46 cm   b) $70 - 30 = 40\,\text{cm}$

c)

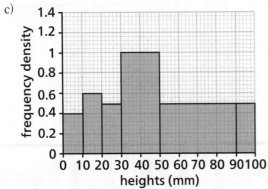

Checkpoint challenge answers

Number				
Question	Working	Answer	Notes	
1	6×4	24	M1	for correct method (multiplying number of colours by number of patterns)
			A1	for 24
2	$2\frac{2}{5} + \frac{3}{4}$ $= 2 + \frac{8}{20} + \frac{15}{20}$ $= 2 + \frac{23}{20}$ $= 3\frac{3}{20}$	$3\frac{3}{20}$	M1	for converting both fractions to get a common denominator of a multiple of 20 with at least one correctly converted.
			M1	(dependent on previous mark) for $2 + \frac{\text{"8"}}{20} + \frac{\text{"15"}}{20}\left(= 2 + \frac{23}{20}\right)$
			A1	for $3\frac{3}{20}$
3		1.75×10^7	M1	for 17 500 000
			A1	for 1.75×10^7
4	$(12.6 - 8.2) \times \frac{100}{8.2}$ $= 53.6585\ldots$	53.7%	M1	for $12.6 - 8.2$ (= 4.4)
			M1	(dependent on previous mark) $\frac{\text{"4.4"}}{8.2} \times 100$ or equivalent
			A1	
5		$\frac{116}{495}$	M1	for $100x = 23.4343434\ldots$ or $1000x = 234.34343434\ldots$ and $10x = 2.34343434\ldots$
			M1	(dependent on previous mark) for subtraction, $100x - x$ or $1000x - 10x$ or $\frac{232}{990}$ seen
			A1	working leading to given fraction
6 a)		$2^2 \times 5 \times 7$	B1	
b)		$2^3 \times 3^2 \times 5^2 \times 7^2$	B1	
c)		$2^3 \times 5^3 \times 7^2$	B1	
d)		$2 \times 3^2 \times 5 \times 7$	B1	
7	$\frac{\sqrt{25} - 4 \times 2}{\sqrt{17}}$	4 − 4.5	B1	rounds appropriately to 5, 4 and 2
			B1	for $\sqrt{17}$
			A1	4 − 4.5
8	$h^2 = (2\sqrt{3})^2 - (\sqrt{3})^2$ $= 12 - 3$ $= 9$ $h = 3$ area $= \frac{1}{2} \times \sqrt{3} \times 3$ $= \frac{3}{2}\sqrt{3}$	$\frac{3}{2}\sqrt{3}$ cm²	M1	for $(2\sqrt{3})^2 - (\sqrt{3})^2$
			M1	for $\frac{1}{2} \times \sqrt{3} \times \sqrt{9}$"
			A1	correct answer only

Checkpoint challenge answers

9		88.3 km/h	B1	for any correct bound clearly identified e.g. 132.4 – 132.45 2 – 2.5
			M1	for method to find upper bound e.g. "132.45" ÷ "1.5"
			A1	for 88.3 km/h
10	a)	9000	B1	for 10^3 or 3^2
			A1	for 9000
	b)	$\dfrac{1}{8}$	A1	
11		–2	M1	for $(2^3)^x = \dfrac{1}{64}$
			A1	$x = -2$

Algebra				
Question		**Working**	**Answer**	**Notes**
1	a)		m^{-8}	B1
	b)		$\dfrac{4}{5}p^{-2}$	B1
2	a)		4	B1
	b)		4	B1
3		$\dfrac{5(x+3)}{20} + \dfrac{4(x+2)}{20}$ $= \dfrac{5x+15}{20} + \dfrac{4x+8}{20}$ $= \dfrac{9x+23}{20}$	$\dfrac{9x+23}{20}$	M1 for use of a common denominator of 20 M1 for $\dfrac{5x+15}{20} + \dfrac{4x+8}{20}$ or equivalent A1
4		$x^2 + 4x - 2x - 8 + bx + a = x^2 + (2+b)x + (a-8)$ $x^2 + 5x - 10 = x^2 + (2+b)x + (a-8)$ $2 + b = 5$ so $b = 3$ $a - 8 = -10$ so $a = -2$	$b = 3$ $a = -2$	M1 for expanding the brackets correctly $x^2 + 2x - 8$ M1 for equating coefficients A1
5	a)		no + written evidence	P1 for start to the process that leads to a decision e.g. $n = \dfrac{(259-5)}{3}$ C1 for a convincing argument for 'No' (e.g. because n is not a whole number)
	b)	$3n + 5 + 3(n+1) + 5 = 6n + 13$	$6n + 13$	M1 for $3n + 5 + 3(n+1) + 5$ or equivalent A1 correct answer only

Checkpoint challenge answers

	c)	$6n + 13 = 85$ $6n = 72$ $n = 12$ $3 \times 12 + 5 = 41$	41	P1	for a process that translates the problem into a suitable form that would lead to a solution e.g. $6n + 13 = 85$
				A1	correct answer only
6	a)		$x_1 = 2.449\,489\,743$	M1	for one correct iteration
			$x_2 = 2.194\,651\,813$	M2	for two further iterations seen
			$x_3 = 2.216\,146\,721$	A1	correct answer only
	b)			C1	statement e.g. iteration is an estimate of the solution
7				B1	for $x + y = 6$ or $x = -2$ or $y = 1$ drawn
				B1	for $x + y = 6$ and $x = -2$ and $y = 1$ drawn
				M1	for consistent shading (in or out) for any two of the lines $x + y = 6$, $x = -2$, $y = 1$
				A1	for lines drawn and correct region shaded
8	a)	$f(2) = 3 + 4$ $\quad = 7$ $g(7) = 3 \times 7 + 1$ $\quad = 22$		P1	for process to begin expansion or showing that $f(2) = 7$
				P1	for showing $g(7) = 22$
	b)	$y = 3 + 2x$ $\dfrac{y - 3}{2} = x$	$f^{-1}(x) = \dfrac{x - 3}{2}$	B1	
9		$(4x - 1)(2x + 1) = 8x^2 + 4x - 2x - 1$		M1	expand two brackets
		$(8x^2 + 4x - 2x - 1)\,(3x + 2)$ $= 24x^3 + 16x^2 + 12x^2 + 8x - 6x^2 - 4x - 3x - 2$	$24x^3 + 22x^2 + x - 2$	M1	expand the third bracket
				A1	correct answer

Checkpoint challenge answers

Ratio and proportion

Question	Working	Answer	Notes
1	$60 \div (9 - 5)$ $(= 15)$ "15" $\times 3$	£45	P1 for a strategy to start to solve problem, e.g. $60 \div (9-5) \ (= 15)$ P1 for full process to solve problem e.g. "15" $\times 3$ A1 correct answer only
2	$5:3 = 20:12$ $4:5 = 12:15$ $A:P:O = 20:12:15$ $\dfrac{20}{47} \times 235$	100	P1 for a strategy to start to solve problem e.g. $20:12$ and $12:15$ P1 for process to solve problem e.g. $\dfrac{20}{47} \times 235$ A1 correct answer only
3	$360 \div 12 = 30\,g$ $550 \times 30 \div 100 = 165$	165	P1 for a strategy to start to solve problem e.g. $360 \div 12$ P1 for process to solve problem e.g. $550 \times 30 \div 100$ A1 correct answer only
4	<table><tr><td>**Equation**</td><td>$y = \dfrac{k}{x}$</td><td>$y = kx$</td><td>$y = kx^2$</td></tr><tr><td>**Graph**</td><td>D</td><td>A</td><td>B</td></tr></table>		B3 for all graphs matched correctly B2 for two graphs matched correctly B1 for one graph matched correctly
5 a)	$y = kx$ $160 = k \times 8$ $k = \dfrac{160}{8}$ $\quad = 20$	$y = 20x$	M1 for $160 = k \times 8$ or equivalent M1 for $y = kx$ or $y \propto x$ A1 for $y = 20x$
b)	$y = 20 \times 15$ $\quad = 300$	300	A1 correct answer only
6		explanation	C1 for a correct evaluation e.g. the value of P should be multiplied by 4
7	$M = \dfrac{k}{n^2}$ $75 = \dfrac{k}{4^2}$ $k = 1200$ $M = \dfrac{1200}{n^2}$ $48 = \dfrac{1200}{n^2}$ $n^2 = \dfrac{1200}{48}$ $n^2 = 25$ $n = \pm 5$	± 5	M1 for $M \propto \dfrac{1}{n^2}$ or $M = \dfrac{k}{n^2}$ M1 for $k = 75 \times 4^2$ $\qquad \quad = 1200$ M1 for $\dfrac{1200}{48}$ A1 for ± 5

Checkpoint challenge answers

8		$486\,\text{cm}^3$	M1 for length ratio $= \sqrt[3]{8}:\sqrt[3]{27} = 2:3$
			M1 for side length of cube 2 ($= 9$)
			M1 for area of one face $= 9^2$ ($= 81$)
			A1 for $486\,\text{cm}^3$
9	$\dfrac{x+1}{x-1} = \dfrac{x+1}{2x}$ $2x(x+1) = (x-1)(x+1)$ $2x^2 + 2x = x^2 - 1$ $x^2 + 2x + 1 = 0$ $(x+1)^2 = 0$ $x = -1$	-1	P1 for process to write an equation
			P1 for process to clear the fractions
			P1 for process to write an equation in the form $x^2 + bx + c$
			P1 for process to solve the equation
			A1 correct answer only

Geometry and measures

Question	Working	Answer	Notes
1		$265°$	M1 for $180° + 085°$
			A1
2		$5\,000\,000\,\text{cm}^3$	M1 for $5 \times 100 \times 100 \times 100$
			A1 or equivalent
3	$34 - 14 - 9 = AC$ ($= 11$) $14^2 - 9^2 = 115$ $11^2 = 121$ $115 \neq 121$	No	M1 for finding missing length
			M1 for substituting lengths into Phythagoras' theorem
			A1 for statement with correct explanation
4		$30°$	M1 for method to identify the interior angle of a regular hexagon e.g. $180 - (360 \div 6)(= 120)$
			M1 for $120 - 90$ ($= 30$)
			A1
5		108π	P1 for equating $\dfrac{4}{3}\pi r^3 = 288\pi$ to find the radius ($= 6$)
			P1 for $A = \dfrac{1}{2}(4\pi r^2) + \pi r^2$
			A1
6		$66°$	M1 for angle DBC $= 180 - 112$ ($= 68$)
			M1 for angle CDB $= 180 - 46 - \text{"}68\text{"}$
			A1 for $x = 66$
			C2 for providing full reasoning (e.g. angles on a straight line sum to 180, angles in a triangle sum to 180, corresponding angles are equal)

Checkpoint challenge answers

7	a)	$(2 + 8) \times 12 \div 2$ $(= 60)$	60 cm²	M1 A1	for a fully correct method for the area
	b)		4	M1	for a correct scale factor or ratio using the two corresponding sides from two similar triangles or two sides within the same triangles
				M1	for a correct equation with AE as the only variable
				A1	correct answer only
	c)		26.6°	M1 A1	for $\tan^{-1}\left(\dfrac{2}{4}\right)$
8			1378 cm³	M1	for finding the length AC = $\sqrt{15^2 + 15^2}$ $= (21.21)$
				M1	for method to find the height of the pyramid $(21.12 \div 2) \times \tan 60$
				A1	for 18.36
				M1	for 15 × 15 × "their height" ÷ 3
				A1	

Probability				
Question	**Working**		**Answer**	**Notes**
1 a)	$1 - (0.12 + 0.23 + 0.4) = 0.25$ $0.25 \div 5 = 0.05$		0.05	M1 for $1 - (0.12 + 0.23 + 0.4)$ or $1 - 0.75$ or 0.25 M1 (dependent on previous mark) for "0.25" ÷ 5 A1
b)	$2(0.4 \times 0.05) + 2(0.2 \times 0.23)$		0.132	M1 for one correct product or a correct pair identified by scores or probabilities M1 for all correct products with intention to add A1
2 a)				B1 table completed correctly

		First set					
		1	**2**	**3**	**6**	**8**	**9**
Second set	**3**	4	5	6	9	11	12
	4	5	6	7	10	12	13
	5	6	7	8	11	13	14
	6	7	8	9	12	14	15

Checkpoint challenge answers

b)			$\frac{1}{12}$	A1 (accept equivalent fractions)
c)			£7	M1 for 120×0.1 (= 12)
				M1 for "$\frac{2}{24}$" $\times 120 \times 0.5$ (= 5)
				A1 correct answer only
3			0.09	M1 for $\sqrt{0.49}$ (= 0.7)
				M1 for $1 - 0.7 = 0.3$
				M1 for 0.3×0.3
				A1
4 a)				B1 for $\frac{1}{3}$ on first branch
				B1 for other branches correct
c)			$\frac{2}{9}$	M1 ft for $\frac{1}{3} \times \frac{2}{3}$
				A1 ft for $\frac{2}{9}$
5 a)			1, 2, 4, 5, 6, 7, 10, 21	B1 (any order)
b)			3, 9	B1 (any order)
c)			$\frac{3}{4}$	A1 (accept equivalent fractions)
6	$\frac{x}{5} \times \frac{x-1}{4} = \frac{x(x-1)}{20}$		$\frac{x(x-1)}{20}$	P1 for $\frac{x}{5}$ or $\frac{x-1}{4}$ or calculation
				P1 for $\frac{x}{5} \times \frac{x-1}{4}$
				A1 or equivalent
7			$\frac{13}{27}$	A1 for $\frac{13}{27}$ or equivalent

First roll, Second roll tree diagram (question 4a):
- First roll: $\frac{2}{3}$ lands on 5; $\frac{1}{3}$ doesn't land on 5
- Second roll (from lands on 5): $\frac{2}{3}$ lands on 5; $\frac{1}{3}$ doesn't land on 5
- Second roll (from doesn't land on 5): $\frac{2}{3}$ lands on 5; $\frac{1}{3}$ doesn't land on 5

Statistics			
Question	**Working**	**Answer**	**Notes**
1 a)		$22 \leqslant a < 26$	B1
b)		20.24 cm	M1 for $x \times f$ using mid-points
			M1 for "$x \times f$" $\div 50$
			A1

Checkpoint challenge answers

2	a)		points plotted	B1	for points plotted correctly
	b)		positive	B1	positive (correlation)
	c)		line of best fit	B1	for line of best fit drawn correctly
	d)		13–14	B1	within range OR
				B1	for correctly reading the value from their line of best fit
3			(Venn diagram)	B4	for all regions correct
				B3	for 5 regions correct
				B2	for 4 regions correct
				B1	for 3 regions correct
4			20	M1	for ordering the ages correctly $x - 6, x + 7, x + 9, x + 10$
				M1	for median $= (2x + 4) \div 2$ or $x + 2$
				M1	for equating $x + 2 = 24$ ($x = 26$)
				A1	correct answer only
5	a)	median = 22, LQ = 13, UQ = 27	box plot	C1	for starting to interpret information e.g. one of the median, LQ, UQ correct
				C1	for starting to communicate information e.g. box plot with box, whiskers and at least 3 of median, LQ, UQ, min and max correct
				C1	correct box plot
	b)		Kevin + reason	C1	Calculation of IQR for Michael = 27 − 13 = 14, or range = 30 − 12 = 18
				C1	for Kevin and comparison
6	a)		(table)	B1	correct answer only
	b)		19	M1	for finding fraction of KS4 girls $\left(\text{i.e. } \dfrac{142}{592}\right)$
				M1	for number of girls in sample $\left(\dfrac{142}{592} \times 80\right)$
				A1	correct answer only

Venn diagram (Question 3):

tennis — hockey — squash

20, 15, 27, 32, 19, 18, 19

Table (Question 6a):

	Male	Female	Total
KS3	128	166	294
KS4	156	142	298
Total	284	308	592

Checkpoint challenge answers

		Time (minutes)	Frequency		
7	a)	$0 < t \leqslant 10$	30	M1	for $300 \div 20 \, (= 15)$ or $300 \div 4 \, (= 75)$
		$10 < t \leqslant 30$	300	B2	for all frequencies correct
		$30 < t \leqslant 40$	300	B1	for at least 2 correct
		$40 < t \leqslant 50$	225		
		$50 < t \leqslant 70$	150		
	b)	52%		M1	for $\dfrac{525}{1005}$
				A1	correct answer only

Practice paper answers

Practice paper 1H			
Question	**Working**	**Answer**	**Notes**
1		Mark: £50 Sarah: £100 Paul: £200	M1 for first step $350 \div (1 + 2 + 4)\ (= 50)$ A1 for 50 A1 for all three correct answers
2	$\dfrac{17}{5} - \dfrac{5}{3} = \dfrac{51}{15} - \dfrac{25}{15}$ $= \dfrac{26}{15}$ $= 1\dfrac{11}{15}$	$1\dfrac{11}{15}$	M1 for conversion to improper fractions $3\dfrac{2}{5} = \dfrac{17}{5}$ $1\dfrac{2}{3} = \dfrac{5}{3}$ M1 for a complete correct method A1 for $\dfrac{26}{15}$ or $1\dfrac{11}{15}$
3		8–8.5	B1 rounds appropriately using two of 100, 3 and 11 M1 $\sqrt{67}$ A1 8–8.5
4	$2x + 5 + 2x + 10 + 37 = 180$ $4x + 52 = 180$ $4x = 128$ $x = 32$ $2x + 10 = 74$	74°	P1 process to start problem solving e.g. forms an appropriate equation P1 complete process to solve equation A1
5		£81	M1 for $\sqrt{15^2 - 12^2}$ A1 for 9 M1 for $\dfrac{1}{2} \times \text{"9"} \times 12\ (= 54)$ M1 for 54×1.50 A1
6		Both lines have a gradient of 4 so they are parallel	M1 for rearranging L_2 to $y = 4x - a$ C1 for comparing gradients and correct statement
7		236 000	A1
8		1.36×10^4	M1 for 13.6 or 10^3 A1
9	$30 \times 25 = 750$ $10 \times 31 = 310$ $750 - 310 = 440$ $440 \div 20 = 22$	22 months	M1 for $30 \times 25\ (= 750)$ or $10 \times 31\ (= 310)$ M1 for $(750 - 310) \div 20$ A1 correct answer only

Practice paper answers

10		70% = £420 10% = £60 100% = £600	£600	M1	for 70% or 0.7 seen
				A1	correct answer only
11	a)	Median = 26 LQ = 23 UQ = 28	Box plot	C1	start to interpret information e.g. one of the median, LQ or UQ correct
				C1	Starts to communicate information e.g. box plot with box, whiskers and at least 3 of median, LQ, UQ, min and max correct
				C1	correct box plot
	b)		Fernando with reason	M1	interpret information e.g. ft from box plot to find IQR (5) or range (9)
				C1	communicates Fernando referring to IQR or range
12		$(x + 2)(x + 3) = x^2 + 5x + 6$ $(x - 4)(x^2 + 5x + 6)$ $= x^3 + 5x^2 + 6x - 4x^2 - 20x - 24$ $= x^3 + x^2 - 14x - 24$	$x^3 + x^2 - 14x - 24$	M1	for expanding two brackets correctly
				M1	for multiplying other bracket by the result of the first M1 – allow one error
				A1	correct answer only
13	a)		3000	M1	for 3 or 1000 or 10^3
				A1	correct answer only
	b)		12	M1	for 6 or 2
				A1	correct answer only
14			–2	M1	for $64 = 2^6$
				A1	correct answer only
15	a)		$\sqrt{\dfrac{3}{2}}$	A1	correct answer only
	b)	$0.5 = \dfrac{x}{10}$ $x = 5$	5	M1	$\cos 60 = \dfrac{x}{10}$
				A1	correct answer only
16		$8x + 12y = -20$ $9x - 12y = 54$ $17x = 34$ $x = 2$	$x = 2, y = -3$	M1	for correct method to eliminate 1 variable
				M1	for correct method to find second variable
				A1	for $x = 2, y = -3$
17		$4x - 2 > 6$ $4x > 8$ $x > 2$ $5x - 3 < 17$ $5x < 20$ $x < 4$	$x = 3$	B1	for $x > 2$ or for $x < 4$
				B1	for $x > 2$ and for $x < 4$
				B1	for $x = 3$

Practice paper answers

18	a)			M1	for $(x-3)^2 - 32 + 2$ or attempt to find points to plot. Must have at least 3 points correctly plotted.
				A1	for $(x-3)^2 - 7$ or parabola with minimum marked at $(3, -7)$
				C1	for parabola drawn with minimum in 1st quadrant or y-intercept at $(0, 2)$
				C1	for parabola drawn with minimum in 1st quadrant and y-intercept at $(0, 2)$
	b)			C1	for a start to explanation e.g. $f(x+1) - 2$ is a translation of $\begin{pmatrix} -1 \\ -2 \end{pmatrix}$ or attempt to draw graph of $f(x+1) - 2$ or graph of $f(x+1)$ and $y = 2$ drawn
				C1	for a convincing explanation e.g. new minimum at $(2, -9)$ so does have real roots
19		$3ab - 4a = b - 6$ $a(3b-4) = b - 6$	$a = \dfrac{b-6}{3b-4}$	M1	collect as onto one side
				M1	for factorising
				A1	
20			$\dfrac{-7\sqrt{5}}{5}$	M1	expands brackets e.g. $2 - 9 = -7$
				M1	rationalises the denominator e.g. using $\sqrt{5}$ as the numerator and denominator
				A1	
21			48π	P1	starts a process by using $\dfrac{128}{3}\pi$ and $\dfrac{1}{2} \times \dfrac{4}{3}\pi r^3$ to find the radius as 4
				P1	starts process using $\dfrac{1}{2}$ curved surface e.g. $(4 \times \pi \times 4^2) \div 2$
				P1	complete process shown e.g. $(4 \times \pi \times 4^2) \div 2 + (\pi \times 4^2)$
				A1	for 48π
22			$135\,\text{cm}^3$	M1	for length scale factor $= \sqrt{\dfrac{9}{16}}$ or $\dfrac{3}{4}$ or $3:4$
				M1	for $\left(\dfrac{4}{9}\right)^3 \times 320$ or $33:43$
				A1	
23			0.01	M1	for $\sqrt{0.81}$ $(= 0.9)$
				M1	for $1 - 0.9 = 0.1$
				M1	for 0.1×0.1
				A1	correct answer only
24	a)	$g(4 - 2 \times 1) = 2(2)2$ $\qquad = 8$		P1	for process to begin expansion e.g. $(4 - 2 \times 1)$
				P1	for full process to stated expression
				A1	
	b)	$\dfrac{4-x}{2} = -1$ $4 - x = -2$ $x = 6$	$x = 6$	P1	for the start of finding $f^{-1}(x) = \dfrac{4-x}{2}$
				M1	for $\dfrac{4-x}{2} = -1$
				M1	for method of solving equation to find x
				A1	

Practice paper answers

Question		Working	Answer	Notes	
1			$\dfrac{37}{100}$	B1	
2			10	B1	
3			11.0025	M1	for 8.7025 or 2.3
				A1	
4	a)		correct drawing	M1	for correct bearing drawn (70° angle)
				A1	for correct position of B (3 cm from A)
	b)		250°	B1	
5		$8000 \times 1.03 \times 1.03 \times 1.03 \times$ $1.03 = 9004.07$	4 years	M1	for 1.03 seen
				A1	
6		$360 \div 6 = 60$	60°	P1	for process to find the exterior angle or interior angle of a hexagon or square
		$180 - 60 = 120$		P1	for process to find x
		$360 - 120 - 90 - 90 = 60$		A1	for 60 from correct working
7	a)	$60 : 40$	$1 : 1.67$ or $1 : \dfrac{2}{3}$	M1	for $60 : (100 - 60)$
		$1 : 1.67$		A1	$1 : 1.67$ or equivalent
	b)		$\dfrac{3}{10}$	A1	
8		$x = \ 0.144444$	shown	M1	for a complete method
		$100x = 14.44444$		A1	fully correct working
		$10x = \ 1.44444$			
		$90x = 13$			
		$x = \dfrac{13}{90}$			
9		$\sqrt{9.65^2 - 5.45^2}$	7.963667497	B1	for finding bounds of one measurement: 5.35, 5.45 or 9.65, 9.75
				P1	for process of choosing and using correct bounds
				P1	for process of Pythagoras' theorem and correct bounds
				A1	for 7.963(667…)
10		$2(x - 5c) = 5 - 3x$		P1	for process to start a chain of reasoning
		$2x - 10c = 5 - 3x$		P1	for process to isolate terms in x
		$5x = 10c + 5$		C1	for convincing explanation from $x = 2c + 1$
		$x = 2c + 1$			

Practice paper answers

11	$2x - 2 = x^2 - 5x + 8$ $x^2 - 7x + 10 = 0$ $(x - 5)(x - 2) = 0$ $x = 5$, or $x = 2$ When $x = 5$, $y = 8$ When $x = 2$, $y = 2$ $8 - 2 = 6$ $5 - 2 = 3$ $6^2 + 3^2 = 36 + 9 = 45$	$\sqrt{45}$	P1 for process to eliminate y. e.g. $2x - 2 = x^2 - 5x + 8$ followed by reduction to 3-term quadratic P1 for factorisation or formula for 3-term quadratic = 0 P1 for a process to find the values of y A1 all four values ($x = 5$, $y = 8$ and $x = 2$, $y = 2$) P1 for a correct process to find the distance^2 or distance between two points A1 for $\sqrt{45}$ or equivalent
12 a)		$4(2s + 3)$	B1
b)		$(x - 3)(x + 7)$	M1 for $(x \pm 3)(x \pm 7)$ A1
13 a)	 _graph: distance (km) vs time of day (am)_		M1 for method to find the distance travelled in 42 minutes e.g. line drawn at the correct gradient or distance travelled $\frac{42}{60} \times 40_h (= 28_h \text{km})$ C1 for correct graph from 8.00 am to 8.42 am C1 for graph drawn from "(8.42, 28)" to (9.45, 84)
b)		15 km	M1 for 60×0.25 oe A1 correct answer only
14 a)	 _graph: cumulative frequency vs length (cm)_		M1 for running total of values: 2, 6, 13, 25, 33, 40 (allow 1 error) M1 for cumulative frequency with at least 5 points plotted correctly at the ends of the intervals C1 for correct graph with points joined by curve or straight-line segments
b)		35–37	B1 35–37
c)		20%	M1 for value of 7–8 seen M1 for "8" ÷ 40 × 100 A1

Practice paper answers

15	total frequency $= a + 23$ sum of values $= 20(a + 23)$ $fx = (12 \times 3) + (16 \times 7) + (20 \times 9) +$ $(24 \times a) + (28 \times 4)$ $= 440 + 24a$ $440 + 24a = 20(a + 23)$ $\quad\quad 4a = 20$ $\quad\quad a = 5$	5	P1	for process to start solving the problem e.g. finding the mid-points 12, 16, 20, 24, 28
			P1	for process to find the sum of values e.g. $20(a + 23)$
			P1	for process to work out the estimated mean from the given values e.g. $440 + 24a$
			A1	
16		$n^2 + 2n + 1$ or $(n + 1)^2$	M1	for correct deduction from differences e.g. second difference is 2 implies $1n^2$ or sight of 12, 22, 32 …
			M1	for sight of 12, 22, 32 … linked with 1, 2, 3 …
			A1	for $n^2 + 2n + 1$ or equivalent
17 a)		$\dfrac{25}{40}$	M1	for beginning to interpret given information e.g. 3 overlapping ovals with central region correct
			M1	for extending the interpretation of given information e.g. 3 overlapping labelled ovals with at least 5 regions correct
			M1	for using the correct method to communicate given information e.g. 3 overlapping labelled ovals with all regions correct.
			A1	for $\dfrac{25}{40}$ or equivalent
b)		$\dfrac{10}{21}$	P1	for correct process to identify correct regions in Venn diagram and divide by "21"
			A1	
18		triangle $(-4, -1)\ (-8, -1)$ $(-4, -5)$	M1	for correct shape and correct orientation in the wrong position or 2 vertices correct
			A1	correct answer only

Practice paper answers

19		9.11 cm²	P1	starts process by using the cosine rule to find CD
				e.g. $(CD)^2 = 7.2^2 + 4.6^2 - 2 \times 7.2 \times 4.6 \times \cos 70$ $(= 50.344\,585\,71)$
			P1	uses sine rule to find angle ACD or angle ADC and using this to find CDB and so CDB
				e.g. $\dfrac{\sin_{\shortmid} C}{4.6} = \dfrac{\sin_{\shortmid} 70}{7.095}$ or $\dfrac{\sin_{\shortmid} D}{7.2} = \dfrac{\sin_{\shortmid} 70}{7.095}$
			P1	uses sine rule to find BC or BD
				e.g. $\dfrac{BD}{\sin_{\shortmid} 18} = \dfrac{7.095}{\sin_{\shortmid} 54.468}$
			P1	for process to find area e.g. $\dfrac{1}{2} ab \sin_{\shortmid} C$
			A1	for 9.11
20	a)	1.3–1.9	M1	for finding the gradient by drawing tangent
			M1	for method to calculate gradient
			A1	for 1.3–1.9
	b)		C1	for acceleration
			C1	for e.g. "3 seconds after the start of the race", "when the speed is 7 m/s", "in m/s²"
	c)		C1	for comment, e.g. dependent on accuracy of constructing a tangent
21	$3 = pq^0$ $3 = p$ $y = 3q^x$ $96 = 3q^5$ $32 = q^5$ $q = 2$ $y = 3 \times 2^3$ $= 24$	24	M1	for substituting (0, 3) or (5, 96)
			M1	for substituting (0, 3) and (5, 96)
			A1	for $p = 3$ and $q = 2$
			A1	correct answer only
22	a)		M1	for method to find at least one root in [1, 2], e.g. $x^3 + 5x - 9 (= 0)$ and f(1) $(= -3)$, f(2) $(= 9)$ oe
			C1	for since there is a change in sign there must be at least one root in $0 < x < 1$ (as f is continuous), or 0 and 6 are either side of 3
	b)	$x_1 = 1.817\,12\ldots$	M1	for one correct iteration
		$x_2 = 1.525\,295\ldots$	M1	for two further iterations
	c)	1.610	A1	

Practice paper answers

Practice paper 3H				
Question	**Working**		**Answer**	**Notes**
1 a)	 A: 4, 28, 8, 16, 20; A∩B: 12, 24; B: 6, 18; outside: 2, 10, 14, 22, 26			B4 for all numbers in the correct place B3 for one omission or error B2 for two omissions or errors B1 for three omissions or errors
b)			$\dfrac{2}{15}$	B1 for 2 seen follow through from a) A1 correct answer only
2			23	P1 for process to find the gradient using the given coordinates e.g. for $\dfrac{s-5}{3}=6$ P1 for process to solve equation to find s A1 correct answer only
3 a)	$2x + 4x - 0.3 + x + 0.1$ $\qquad + 3x - 0.2 = 1$ $\qquad 10x - 0.4 = 1$ $\qquad\qquad 10x = 1.4$ $\qquad\qquad\quad x = 0.14$ $4x - 0.3 = 0.56 - 0.3 = 0.26$		0.26	M1 for summing probabilities and equating to 1 M1 for $x = 0.14$ A1
b)	$0.14 + 0.1 = 0.24$ $0.24 \times 500 = 120$		120	M1 for 0.24×500 A1
4	distance Manchester to Leeds $= 40 \times 1.25 = 50$ miles time Leeds to Nottingham $= 100 \div 50$ $\qquad\qquad\qquad\qquad\quad = 2$ hours distance Leeds to Nottingham $= 100$ miles total distance $= 150$ miles total time $= 3.25$ hours average speed $= 150 \div 3.25$ $\qquad\qquad\qquad = 46.1538\ldots$		46 mph	M1 for method to find the distance from Manchester to Leeds M1 for method to find the time from Leeds to Nottingham A1 for 150 miles and 3.25 hours M1 for "150" ÷ "3.25" A1 for 46
5			24.4 cm	M1 for $\dfrac{280}{360} \times \pi \times 10$ or $\dfrac{80}{360} \times \pi \times 10$ A1
6 a)			$\begin{pmatrix} 6 \\ -1 \end{pmatrix}$	B1
b)			$\begin{pmatrix} -8 \\ -12 \end{pmatrix}$	B1 for $\begin{pmatrix} 4 \\ -6 \end{pmatrix}$ or $\begin{pmatrix} 12 \\ -6 \end{pmatrix}$ A1

MATHS HIGHER

Practice paper answers

7		reflection in the x-axis	M1 for reflection or rotation of shape A
			A2 for reflection in the x-axis Special case: 1 mark for just reflection
8 a)		8.1 cm	M1 for comparing ratios of sides or $10.2 \div 3.4 = 3$
			M1 for 3×2.7
			A1 correct answer only
b)		2.6 cm	M1 for comparing ratios of sides e.g. $\frac{7.8}{8.1} = \frac{AB}{2.7}$ or $\frac{7.8}{10.2} = \frac{AB}{3.4}$
			A1 correct answer only
9	$\frac{1}{4} \times \frac{1}{8} \times \frac{1}{7} \times \frac{1}{6} = \frac{1}{1344}$	$\frac{1}{1344}$	M1 for $\frac{4}{9}$ seen and recognition that each number can only be used once
			A1
10		7.19 cm	M1 for $\sin 64 = \frac{AB}{8}$
			A1 correct answer only
11	Bank A $5000 \times 1.025^4 = 5519.06$ Bank B $5000 \times 1.038 \times 1.013^3 = 5395.05$	Bank A	M1 for 1.025 or 1.038 or 1.013
			M1 for working out the amount in each bank after 4 years
			C1 communicates Bank A (dependent on previous M1)
12 a)	1st pick 2nd pick $\frac{5}{12}$ red $\frac{4}{11}$ red $\frac{7}{11}$ yellow $\frac{7}{12}$ yellow $\frac{5}{11}$ red $\frac{6}{11}$ yellow	correct tree diagram	M1 for the first branch correct
			M1 for the second branch correct
b)	$\frac{5}{12} \times \frac{4}{11} + \frac{7}{12} \times \frac{6}{11}$	$\frac{62}{132}$ or equivalent	M1 for $\frac{5}{12} \times \frac{4}{11}$ or $\frac{7}{12} \times \frac{6}{11}$
			A1
13		$2.185 \leqslant n < 2.195$	M1 for 2.185
			M1 for 2.195
			A1 for correct order and symbols

MATHS HIGHER

Practice paper answers

14	$\dfrac{8x-2}{6}+\dfrac{9x+6}{6}=\dfrac{10x+18}{6}$ $8x-2+9x+6=10x+18$ $7x=14$ $x=2$	$x=2$	M1 for finding a common denominator e.g. 6, 12 M1 for writing as a linear equation without fractions M1 for solving equation A1 correct answer only
15		$x+y>3$ $y-x<2$ $x<3$	B1 for $x+y=3$ or $y-x=2$ or $x=3$ B1 for $x+y>3$ B1 for $y-x<2$ B1 for $x<3$
16	$R:T=2:5$ or $16:40$ $T:C=8:10$ or $40:50$ $R:C=16:50$ or $8:25$	$8:25$	P1 for process to find a multiple of 5 and 8 P1 for process to compare ratios of roses to carnations A1 correct answer only
17 a)	$\dfrac{(x+3)(x-3)}{(2x+1)(x-3)}=\dfrac{(x+3)}{(2x+1)}$	$\dfrac{(x+3)}{(2x+1)}$	M1 for $(x+3)(x-3)$ M1 for $(2x\pm1)(x\pm3)$ A1
18	$t=\dfrac{3(2u-s)}{s}$ $st=3(2u-s)$ $st=6u-3s$ $st+3s=6u$ $s(t+3)=6u$ $s=\dfrac{6u}{t+3}$	$s=\dfrac{6u}{t+3}$	M1 for isolating s M1 for factorising A1 correct answer only
19	$\text{area}=\dfrac{1}{2}ab\sin C$ $\qquad=\dfrac{1}{2}\times\sqrt{\dfrac{3}{2}}\times(2x+1)(x-2)$ $\dfrac{\sqrt{3}}{4}(2x+1)(x-2)=2\sqrt{3}$ $2x^2-3x-2=8$ $2x^2-3x-10=0$ $x=\dfrac{+3\pm\sqrt{9-4(2\times-10)}}{2\times2}$ $x=\dfrac{+3\pm\sqrt{89}}{4}$ $x=3.11$	$x=3.11$	M1 for using $\dfrac{1}{2}ab\sin C$ M1 for area $=\dfrac{1}{2}\times\sqrt{\dfrac{3}{2}}\times(2x+1)(x-2)=2\sqrt{3}$ M1 for $2x^2-3x-10=0$ M1 for using the formula or completing the square A1

MATHS HIGHER

Practice paper answers

20	a)	$x^2 - 4x + 3 = x^2 - 3x + 4 - x - 1$			$x = 1, x = 3$	M1	draw $y = x + 1$
						A1	
	b)				3–3.2	M1	draws a tangent at $(3, 4)$
						M1	finds the gradient of the tangent
						A1	
21		$4^2 + 2^2 = 20$			$x^2 + y^2 = 20$	M1	for $4^2 + 2^2$
						A1	

22	a)			

Percentage	Frequency
$0 < t \leqslant 20$	12
$20 < t \leqslant 30$	12
$30 < t \leqslant 50$	16
$50 < t \leqslant 80$	12
$80 < t \leqslant 100$	24

all frequencies and bars correct

M1   for $12 \div 10 \ (= 1.2)$

B1   for at least 2 frequencies and bars correct

B1   for all frequencies and bars correct

22 b)   37%   M1   for $\dfrac{28}{76}$ followed through from part a)

A1

Progress and observations

Published by Pearson Education Limited, 80 Strand, London, WC2R 0RL.

www.pearsonschools.co.uk

Text © Pearson Education Limited 2018
Series consultant: Margaret Reeve
Edited by Elektra Media Ltd
Designed by Andrew Magee
Typeset by Elektra Media Ltd
Produced by Elektra Media Ltd
Original illustrations © Pearson Education Limited 2018
Illustrated by Elektra Media Ltd
Cover design by Andrew Magee
Printed in the UK by Ashford Press Ltd

The right of Sharon Bolger to be identified as author of this work has been asserted by her in accordance with the
Copyright, Designs and Patents Act 1988.

First published 2018

21 20 19 18
10 9 8 7 6 5 4 3 2 1

British Library Cataloguing in Publication Data
A catalogue record for this book is available from the British Library

ISBN 978-1-292-19578-0

The ActiveBook accompanying this book contains editable Word files. Pearson Education Limited cannot accept
responsibility for the quality, accuracy or fitness for purpose of the materials contained in the Word files once edited. To
revert to the original Word files, download the files again.

Printed in the United Kingdom by Ashford Press Ltd

Acknowledgements
We would like to thank Tutora for its invaluable help in the development and trialling of this course.

Copies of official specifications for all Pearson qualifications may be found on the website: qualifications.pearson.com

Notes from the publisher
1. While the publishers have made every attempt to ensure that advice on the qualification and its assessment is accurate,
   the official specification and associated assessment guidance materials are the only authoritative source of information
   and should always be referred to for definitive guidance.

   Pearson examiners have not contributed to any sections in this resource relevant to examination papers for which they
   have responsibility.

2. Pearson has robust editorial processes, including answer and fact checks, to ensure the accuracy of the content in
   this publication, and every effort is made to ensure this publication is free of errors. We are, however, only human,
   and occasionally errors do occur. Pearson is not liable for any misunderstandings that arise as a result of errors in this
   publication, but it is our priority to ensure that the content is accurate. If you spot an error, please do contact us at
   resourcescorrections@pearson.com so we can make sure it is corrected.